The Open University

Block 6
Case studies of design and designing

Case studies 1–4 by Steve Garner
Case study 5 by Georgy Holden

T211 Design and designing

This publication forms part of an Open University course T211 *Design and designing*. Details of this and other Open University courses can be obtained from the Student Registration and Enquiry Service, The Open University, PO Box 197, Milton Keynes MK7 6BJ, United Kingdom: tel. +44 (0)845 300 60 90, email general-enquiries@open.ac.uk

Alternatively, you may visit the Open University website at http://www.open.ac.uk where you can learn more about the wide range of courses and packs offered at all levels by The Open University.

To purchase a selection of Open University course materials visit http://www.ouw.co.uk, or contact Open University Worldwide, Walton Hall, Milton Keynes MK7 6AA, United Kingdom for a brochure. tel. +44 (0)1908 858793; fax +44 (0)1908 858787; email ouw-customer-services@open.ac.uk

The Open University
Walton Hall, Milton Keynes
MK7 6AA

First published 2004. Second edition 2009.

Edited and designed by The Open University.

Printed and bound in the United Kingdom by The Charlesworth Group, Wakefield.

ISBN 978 0 7492 2083 9

2.1

Contents

Introduction

In one respect Block 6 provides a conclusion to the course. Five case studies of design and designing are presented here and each one illustrates, to a greater or lesser extent, the principles and practices that have been identified and discussed in the preceding blocks.

But Block 6 is also a starting point. It's a starting point for unravelling the messy and convoluted nature of real-world design and designing. To any readers who have not studied Blocks 1 to 5 these case studies might seem to lack consistency or to present largely unique characteristics. However, to your trained eye you should now be able to identify similarities in, for example, practices, objectives, strategies and relationships. Block 6 provides a starting point for you to look at the world of design and designing with new insight – seeing the commonalities in design practice across widely differing contexts, but also being able to appreciate the individual influences active in any particular example.

The five case studies presented here are snapshots of professional practice. They illustrate the difficult and often frustrating sequences of activities that must be confronted by designers and those they work with. Some reveal extensive teamworking while other studies highlight the way individuals can balance and integrate disparate tasks and responsibilities.

These case studies make no claim to be representative of professional design practice today. They have been selected partly for their breadth – they vary in company size, the type of client, the scale of the product and the volume of the outputs. However, by this stage of the course you should be able to discern many similarities in the design tools used and the design processes in place.

All of the case studies are based on interviews and other data collection by members of the course team. Where possible each study has examples of outputs, including developmental drawings and three-dimensional models as well as the resulting products. Most studies include extended quotations and these have been used by the course team to illustrate the application of theory (as discussed in the course) in practice.

The supplement to Block 6 includes a selection of observations written by members of the course team. The observations make connections between Block 6 and the earlier blocks.

Integral with Block 6 is the design project that forms TMA 06. Both Block 6 and TMA 06 seek to consolidate the skills and knowledge that you have developed during the course. The assignment aims to allow you to demonstrate your designing skills and for this reason the following learning outcomes include specific references to the design project.

Aims and learning outcomes

Aims

The aims of this block are:

1 to illustrate the application of design theories and principles via an examination of particular examples of professional design practice, and to enable you to be able to identify these theories and principles;

2 to enable you to be able to identify commonalities and unique qualities in the design processes of selected examples of practice;

3 to illustrate the various types of model and modelling activity exploited in modern design practice;

4 to enable you to make critical judgements regarding the choice and use of materials and production processes in design and designing;

5 to facilitate the development and application of design skills and knowledge relevant to investigating, planning, creating, evaluating and producing various types of products;

6 to define the characteristics of design and designing today, particularly in the field of product design and to help you to speculate on future pressures and developments;

7 to identify, with examples, the extent to which environmental issues and sustainability are significant factors in modern product design and development.

Learning outcomes

1 Knowledge and understanding

You should be able to demonstrate knowledge and understanding of:

1.1 the main stages of progressing a design from an idea to a manufactured product;

1.2 common or shared design process characteristics across a range of contexts;

1.3 the application of models and modelling in professional design practice;

1.4 the applications for computers in modern design practice and the various outputs available;

1.5 the role of creative thinking and action in selected examples of design;

1.6 sustainability issues and their importance in modern design practice.

2 Cognitive (thinking) skills

You should be able to:

2.1 map the theoretical stages of design activity onto selected examples of design practice;

2.2 compare and contrast examples of professional design practice, particularly noting differences and similarities in design processes;

2.3 apply basic research and investigative activities, introduced earlier in the course, to given design briefs;

2.4 combine creative skills and knowledge to generate and develop design proposals based on research findings;

2.5 transfer understanding of sustainability from one application to another.

3 Key skills

You should be able to:

3.1 apply analytical skills in examining selected examples of design processes and designed products;

3.2 work more effectively and systematically where problems are ill-defined by learning from examples;

3.3 demonstrate various ICT skills including the use of computers for assisting research, communication, documentation and creative work;

3.4 apply knowledge and skills in the identification and resolving of a design problem from a given topic;

3.5 demonstrate written and graphic communication skills.

4 Practical skills

You should have gained:

4.1 an ability to apply various modelling skills, for example drawing and 3D modelling as part of a design project.

Case study 1
Dyson DC05 cyclone cleaner

1.1 Introduction

Of all the UK companies that claim design is central to their organisation Dyson Ltd must be one of the most frequently cited in the popular and professional press. The rate of growth of the company over the past decade and the phenomenal success of many of its products has created interest not only in the business and finance pages of newspapers but in the sections on news, technology, international affairs and the gossip columns. It has been estimated that Dyson products have generated several billion dollars worth of sales worldwide.

Much of this success has to do with the man at the head of the organisation – James Dyson (Figure 1). As its founder and managing director James Dyson, with a personal fortune estimated at £700 million, has been the subject of articles in newspapers and magazines, and programmes on television. You will already have come across him in video sequences on the course DVD ('New Designers' and 'James Dyson: designer and innovator') and in Block 3. You'll find below a little background information on James Dyson and the establishment of the Dyson company but the main purpose of this case study is to chart the development of one particular product, the Dyson DC05 cyclone cleaner (Figure 2). This will provide you with some insights into design and designing at Dyson Ltd.

Figure 1 James Dyson

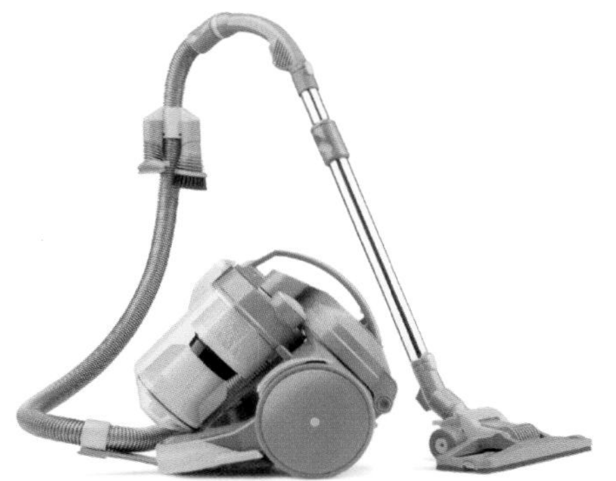

Figure 2 Dyson DC05 cyclone cleaner

1.2 Company background

After studying design at the Royal College of Art, James Dyson worked in product development in the engineering industry. One of his early successes was a boat – the *Sea Truck*. Going solo for the first time in the mid-1970s, Dyson created the Ballbarrow (shown in Section 2 of Block 3 and on the DVD video sequence). The idea for a bagless vacuum cleaner was inspired by problems Dyson encountered when he was renovating his home in 1978. The bag of his conventional vacuum cleaner needed frequent emptying if it was to work efficiently. The cyclone principle had proved an efficient means of separating dust and air in numerous industrial situations. As a result of installing a cyclone separator in his Ballbarrow factory, Dyson saw an opportunity to transfer this technology to the domestic market.

Dyson had struggled to convince anyone to build his early designs, so in 1993 he opened his own factory near his home in the Cotswolds and the DC01 quickly became the fastest selling vacuum cleaner ever to be made in the UK. Recent problems regarding labour costs have forced the company to cut jobs and move production to Asia, but there is still a flourishing design department at a new base in Malmesbury, Wiltshire (Figure 3). More recent products include the Root Cyclone vacuum cleaner, the Contrarotator washing machine and the DC06 robot vacuum cleaner, which guides itself around a room.

Figure 3 Dyson Ltd design centre, Wiltshire, England

Dyson vacuum cleaners represent many aspects of good design – not least because they are commercially successful and they are attractive to users. Many models appear in the permanent collections of museums around the world.

1.3 Design at Dyson

As with so many fields of business practice today secrecy is vital. If a competitor finds out about a new product it could prove disastrous to investments in research and development (R&D), marketing plans and, ultimately, the commercial success of a product. Even a leak that development is ongoing in a certain product area might be sufficient for a competitor to spoil the launch of a new item or to focus its own R&D in that direction thereby eroding the lead of the originator of the work. At Dyson, employees with access to new product development are instructed not to discuss any aspects of it with friends and family in case small but valuable nuggets of information should find their way to the eager ears of UK and overseas competitors. The DCO5, however, is now well established and gaining access to information was straightforward.

1.3.1 Teamworking

In the early days James Dyson worked largely independently or with a small team (as shown in the DVD sequence for Block 3), but nowadays the working practices at Dyson Ltd are founded on a strong commitment to teamworking. There are teams in research, product development and production engineering, who work closely together when necessary. Of the 500 or so scientists and engineers employed at the Wiltshire centre approximately 100 might be referred to as design engineers; around 80 other engineers are employed in research and development with about 70 more employed as test engineers and technicians.

The R&D group consists of individuals and groups with specialist knowledge of, for example, mechanical and electronic engineering, materials science, acoustics, fluid mechanics, chemical engineering, thermal energy and software design. Consequently even those team members representing engineering can display a surprisingly diverse range of skills, knowledge and approaches. These specialist engineers frequently act as consultants to various design and development teams operating simultaneously at Dyson. There might be 10 design teams working at any one time.

1.3.2 Role of the design engineers

Design at Dyson means converting technological principles into products people want to own and use. This requires the workforce involved in design to have a wide range of skills, specialist knowledge, and the motivation to see a project through. Of all the engineers the design engineers probably have the broadest range of activities. In any given project they may assist with defining user requirements, formalising the brief, translating basic principles, applying new materials, defining components or configurations and ensuring new products meet production or assembly requirements. Design engineers partly represent the end user and they partly represent the manufacturer. Their work is directly concerned with resolving conflicts that inevitably arise in product design and development.

The design engineers are drawn from a range of backgrounds reflecting the diverse responsibilities of this group. Some will have studied industrial or product design at a university. Some have a first degree in a specialist engineering discipline such as mechanical engineering and have a postgraduate qualification in design.

At Dyson there are also design engineers who have worked their way up via apprenticeships or come via other, non-design routes. They bring to their respective teams a wide range of knowledge and approaches. Such breadth is viewed positively at Dyson. It's seen not as a loss of potential depth in skills and knowledge but as a means of bringing new qualities essential to teamworking. It can provide, for example, the foundation for good management skills, a sensitivity to the priorities of others and enable good communication within teams.

The benefits and issues of designing in teams were discussed in Block 3 and illustrated in the DVD sequences 'Philips: creative product design' and 'IDEO: creative design teams', and their associated course team comments.

Trading off depth for breadth does have its implications. It means design engineers need to be able to learn from other specialists. They need to be able to distil the important from the unimportant. They need to be able to evaluate the work of others and apply the relevant information.

Design engineering at Dyson, as with other leading consumer product manufacturers, is an increasingly demanding activity as the range and detail of information put into the design arena grows. Not only must information be understood but also it must be evaluated; conflicts must be resolved and actions must be defined. The structuring of design engineering is vital if the activity is to be successful. At Dyson the social processes of design engineering are facilitated by the way team members are regularly brought into close contact. Even the open-plan layout of the design centre aims to encourage interaction (Figure 4).

Figure 4 Design team at work at Dyson

1.4 Beginning of the DCO5 project

Figure 5 Dyson DCO2 cyclone cleaner, 1995

As you saw in Block 2 a design project doesn't properly begin with a brief. A brief needs to be formulated and converted into a marketing and technical specification. This often requires an extended process of investigation and analysis of the current situation that will inevitably refer to both the demand side of the equation, such as consumer needs, and the supply side, such as in-house research and development.

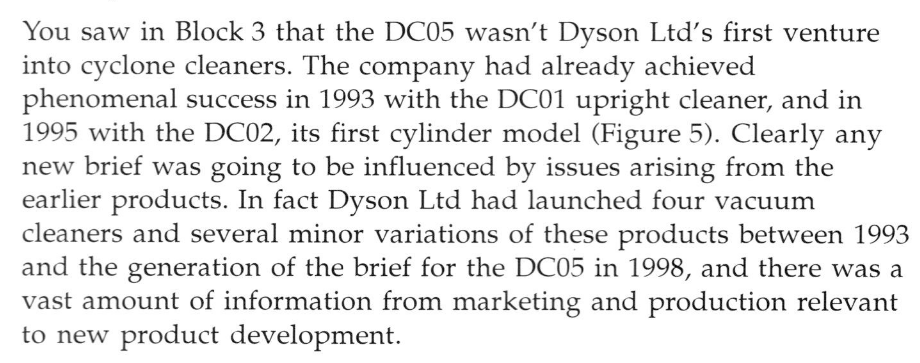

You saw in Block 3 that the DC05 wasn't Dyson Ltd's first venture into cyclone cleaners. The company had already achieved phenomenal success in 1993 with the DC01 upright cleaner, and in 1995 with the DC02, its first cylinder model (Figure 5). Clearly any new brief was going to be influenced by issues arising from the earlier products. In fact Dyson Ltd had launched four vacuum cleaners and several minor variations of these products between 1993 and the generation of the brief for the DC05 in 1998, and there was a vast amount of information from marketing and production relevant to new product development.

The initial development team for the DC05 consisted of one project manager, two senior design engineers and six other design engineers. With a team of nine it was easy for them to gather together to give shape to the outline brief. In fact the team relied on regularly getting round a table to throw ideas into the melting pot from which the design specification emerged. The original brief for the team was to devise a cyclone cleaner based on the DC02 that was 'smaller, lighter, quieter and more powerful'.

The movement away from the upright configuration was based on market studies in Japan. In fact the UK is unusual in its demand for upright vacuum cleaners – most other countries prefer a configuration where the cylinder is located close to the floor and a light vacuum nozzle is connected via a flexible hose. One of the drivers in this brief was Dyson Ltd's Japan office that believed a smaller, cylinder product would be well received in a Japanese market. The Japanese had already demonstrated their acceptance of the Dyson design phenomenon by contributing the equivalent of several million pounds in sales of Dyson vacuum cleaners. It's possible the efficiency of the dust collection system was appealing. Alternatively, it may have been the novelty of the design and styling – particularly the bold use of colour and form – which stood out in the Japanese market swamped with lookalike consumer products. Either way, it added weight to a company impression that a better version of the DC02 cleaner could be well worth the investment.

1.4.1 Concept design for the DC05

The generation of concept ideas for the DC05 took place in parallel with the development of the design specification – an illustration of designing as the simultaneous evolution of problem and solution. At this stage the team worked to establish key properties of the product (as discussed in Block 2). These included specifying:

- dust capacity of the new product;
- motor – power, size, technology;
- filter to capture the smallest of dust particles;
- cable retraction and storage.

Outside of the team discussions of the specification, individual members were encouraged to generate ideas in the form of sketch drawings and basic three-dimensional models. These were then brought to team meetings for presentation and discussion (see Figure 6).

Figure 6 Concept sketches for the DC05

This is a well-accepted design strategy where teams are involved. If the team had worked together on producing one concept model it is likely that alternative and potentially valuable ideas would be dismissed simply because they were not compatible with the single concept being explored. This strategy of allowing individuals to work up their own ideas means alternative perceptions of the problem get an airing and a broader range of concepts is presented for consideration.

Within six weeks of the initial briefing the team had pooled individual ideas and was able to generate a basic full-size form model that communicated the general arrangement of the component parts. The team refer to this model as a development space model.

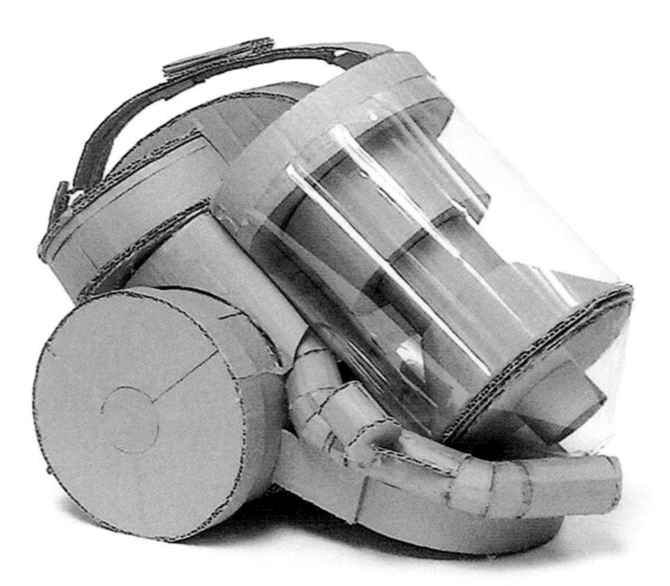

Figure 7 Early development space model of the DC05 made in cardboard

1.4.2 Early development space model

You first came across the model in Figure 7 in the *Modelling Workbook* and you can probably tell from the photograph that this was a quick and cheap model. The various parts including the casing are not, as you might expect, carefully made in plastic and metal. It is largely made from corrugated cardboard with a thin sheet of clear plastic film bent around to give an impression of the transparent cyclone casing. The wheels are not real wheels but made from sheets of cardboard. The whole construction is held together with hot-melt glue and double-sided adhesive tape.

You may be surprised that a company with sophisticated model-making facilities at its disposal should bother to make such rough models but consider this justification by one of the design engineers at Dyson:

> When I'm modelling in card I'm still exploring the problem. It's part of my creativity. Sometimes I can draw my ideas and I use this to clarify my own thinking and to share ideas with others. But at other times I'm thinking and making at the same time. I couldn't ask someone to make the model for me because I'm designing it as I'm making it.
>
> (David Mlynski, design engineer, July 2002)

The importance of rough sketching and 3D modelling at the early concept stage of design was discussed in Block 3. The card construction of the DC05 shown above reveals some of the qualities of the personal modelling strategy described by the design engineer. There is a sense of incompleteness, of the idea being unresolved. This needn't be a disadvantage. Allowing parts of the design to be vague or unresolved has two advantages: firstly it allows the maker and the viewers to more clearly focus their attention on those elements that are more resolved or under discussion, and secondly by only vaguely modelling components the designers build-in ambiguity. Team members might view this ambiguity in many different and positive ways resulting in a number of interpretations and ideas from one model.

The development space model wasn't the first model to be made by members of the DC05 team. However, the rough models from the earliest stage of design rarely last long. Sometimes, like sketching, they have a personal function. They are temporary and are often too flimsy to last. Evidence of such early modelling can be the most difficult to find because it is usually thrown away when the team move on to more robust models.

The model shown in Figure 7 was made some way into the creative process. This isn't one designer's conjecture. This model reflects the team's attempt to combine the best ideas that emerged from the earlier individual activity and group discussions. Models such as this might be made by one or more members of the team, delegated to follow the consensus of the team and guided by agreed sketches. What it communicates to the team (and quite well to you and me as viewers) is a proposal for a certain configuration of components. It allows the team to produce an initial list of parts – and to begin the process of specifying the material from which each part will be made.

One of the key advantages of such card models is that if it's completely wrong it can be thrown in the bin and the design team have wasted only a few costly hours of development time. Contrast this with the likely costs of making a lifelike or perhaps a working model only to find there was a fundamental error in the conceptualisation of the brief, the interpretation of market needs or the manufacturability of the product. Card models such as this have a vital role to play in the commercial design process – particularly at the concept stage.

The development space model was produced about six weeks into the design process of the DC05. With nine people on the team the number of person hours costed to the project rapidly increased. At Dyson such teams are flexible with members moving in and out as required, but even so the card model represents a considerable number of person hours and therefore many thousands of pounds of investment by the company.

The model's existence has to be justified, even though it is a physical embodiment of the team's shared understanding and represents the configuration. It represents the decisions about how big the motor might need to be and how big the dust collection cylinder might be. It facilitates questions such as: could the wheels be smaller, how is access to the filter arranged, and where will the cable retract to? Clearly it facilitates enhanced communication within the team, which can begin to debate subtle changes to configurations and identify strengths and weaknesses.

This model was also shown to senior management, including James Dyson himself. Often, conceptual problems concerning compatibility with future manufacturing or marketing strategies are identified at this stage. The card model might be used to generate information that helps sort out a feature or clarify the specification, which in turn guides the detail design.

The development space model enabled the Dyson team to generate a more detailed plan and to identify the specialist expertise that was to become involved in the subsequent development. It enabled the project manager to know what resources had to be committed.

1.5 Building detail into concepts

It is interesting to explore the use of computers in this early stage of concept development. On the face of it there has been little exploitation of computer-aided design (CAD). Dyson Ltd's investment in CAD modelling and rapid-prototyping technologies has not led to an abandoning of traditional design techniques.

As you saw in the essay by Mark Evans in the *Modelling Workbook* it is quite possible for companies to integrate the two. Where it is deemed desirable Dyson Ltd uses sophisticated CAD modelling to generate virtual models quickly – models that only exist in the computer. However, as you saw in Block 5, such virtual models can be quickly and effectively converted into tangible 3D forms via any one of a number of rapid-prototyping processes. Such models are viewed as complementary to, rather than a replacement of, handmade rough models.

Any physical model offers the potential for direct feedback – a 3D model can be picked up, user interaction simulated, and manufacture and assembly problems can be more apparent.

Of course, the DC05 was to use existing cyclone technology for which a great deal of computer modelling had already taken place that could be adapted to suit the DC05. It's interesting to contrast this style of product development with that of the original cyclone vacuum cleaner by James Dyson himself (shown in detail on the DVD sequence 'James Dyson: designer and innovator'). In this, Dyson exploited a systematic trial-and-error method, making thousands of model cyclones and test rigs and working prototypes to create a product out of a basic idea.

Dyson Ltd operates a policy of not introducing technical constraints at the concept design stage. It believes product innovation is more likely if its teams can work unhindered by constraints that may or may not prove to be significant later down the line. One example of this is the relative freedom given to the design team in reducing the cyclone system so that it would be compatible with the projected small size of the DC05 product. Up to this point most of the Dyson cleaners had been upright models that offered considerable space in which to place the cyclone mechanism – in upright cleaners the handle is usually about one metre above the vacuum head. This wasn't the case in the DC02 and the DC05 aimed to be even more compact, requiring a reduction in cyclone size while ideally increasing its power. By this stage a two-way dialogue had begun between the cyclone engineers and the design team in order to integrate the conceptual and the practical.

At this stage a different type of model was required. The development space models had demonstrated that the configuration of cyclone, motor, chassis, wheels, and so on would be worth further exploration, so a different type of rough model was produced, mostly from medium-density fibreboard (MDF).

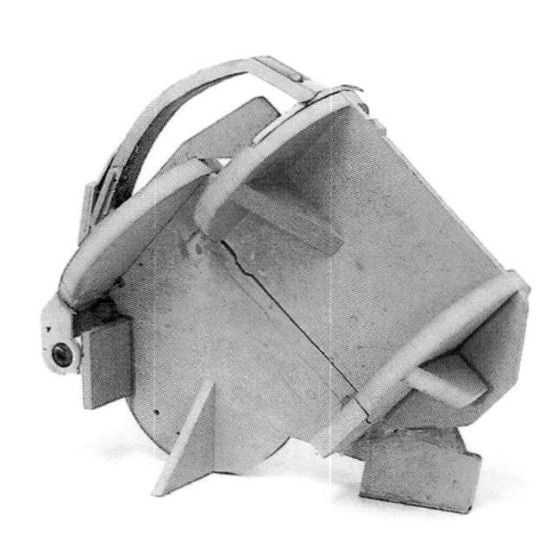

Figure 8 Part of a rough MDF model for the DC05

This model represented the actual weights and handling characteristics of the DC05 proposal. It enabled tests on its overall balance when being used, including when being carried. These tests led to modification to the concept and they contributed to configuration and component design. You can see from Figure 8 that this isn't a very sophisticated model and not a pretty model either. It helped the design team establish the volumes of the main components and the likely interaction between components. Again this is a relatively low-cost model. You can see that assembling shapes cut from sheets of 12 mm and 18 mm MDF define the volumes and that gluing corner braces between the component parts increases strength.

Information was building up rapidly because other specialist groups within the company were contributing. For example, the rough, concept models allowed production engineers to present their perceptions of strengths and weaknesses regarding the manufacturability of key components; other specialists were able to comment on or ask questions about, for example, materials or marketing. These were not random contributions because they were an intended consequence of gearing up the development of the DC05 in the company. The accumulating information required ordering and filing so that it could be accessed when required. Project administration can be a large and vital task in product development, often requiring the services of a technical administrator.

1.6 Principle-proving models and prototyping

At this point the project had been running for about 12 weeks. Some of the mechanical principles had been determined early in the concept design; for example how the dust collection bin was to be removed and the use of large rear wheels. Others were worked out using drawings or simple two-dimensional constructions to explore how parts might move or where linkages might be needed. A number of principle-proving models were also made. These allowed the design team to begin to combine some of the detail information emerging within the company, particularly concerning the space envelope of components and the combinations of components.

As mentioned earlier, one of the values of quick and cheap models is their ability to support and encourage dialogue within the design team. Not only do individuals begin to 'see' problems and opportunities but also other people can point towards essential research or development before it's too late. At this stage discussion is vital. This team believed it was essential for junior designers not to be shy about offering their opinion to senior designers because at this stage it's not too late or too costly to modify the concept design.

The construction of a principle-proving model is partly an extension of the rough modelling activity undertaken from the outset of a project. Like all models, they are incomplete in some way. Principle-proving models are usually crude lash-ups of available parts, roughly modified so that the working principle can be evaluated. Their purpose is to generate data about the operation of an idea; they are not primarily concerned with creatively exploring ideas or even developing them. At Dyson, the principle-proving models and the early prototyping merge into one another. It's difficult to see where one objective finishes and another begins.

As with the principle-proving models, the objective in early prototyping is to test working principles as opposed to the visual qualities of the physical form. Consequently prototypes can look quite messy. Frequently they will use components that function in the appropriate way but look nothing like the components that will eventually be used. This means prototypes must be used selectively. They might, for example, provide good information about power consumption but provide irrelevant information about the ergonomics of user interaction or the weight of the product.

Figure 9 Early working prototype of the DC05

1.6.1 Prototype of the DC05

The early working prototype of the DC05 in Figure 9 was built from bits of other vacuum cleaners in the Dyson range as well as some specially commissioned new parts. Some of the existing components were usable without modification while others were cut and shaped out of all recognition. You can see from the illustration that the final assembly is rather crude – it certainly doesn't attempt to show the defined components of the final product. Some of the components are held together with plastic tape and filler is used to plug gaps thereby improving the vacuum in the prototype. There is no attempt to make the prototype look better by, for example, painting it. This sort of prototype requires time and specialist skill to build and Dyson Ltd uses professional prototypers and modellers for just this purpose.

I suggested earlier that there is a symbiotic relationship between the use of computer-aided design techniques and the construction of physical models and prototypes at Dyson. The conduct of one informs the other. The DC05 moved from being a concept design to one that had detail via both modelling processes.

Sophisticated Unigraphics CAD software was used to model some of the components and these CAD models assisted the design team to reassess, for example, the interaction of parts and the fit between components. The definition of this broad level of detail via the making of digital models informed the construction of form models and prototypes (discussed below), which in turn provided more information about the configuration of parts and led to modifications to the CAD models. It's at this stage that even more people become involved in the project and for this reason it's essential all are working from the same shared database of dimensions, components and specifications. To do otherwise would mean one group's findings or proposals will not match the models or outputs generated by another group.

The prototype of the DC05 was built to investigate four aspects of functionality:

- suction power
- noise
- cyclone performance
- blockages

It was at this prototype stage that the design team worked closely with specialists brought in from research and development departments for testing and validation. Experts in fluid dynamics, for example, contributed to the conversion of a large cyclone mechanism to a more compact system suitable for the DC05. This phase of development particularly concerned the cyclone geometry and the filter requirements.

1.6.2 Using foam models to assess ideas

Simultaneous with this development the design engineers were attempting to define the overall product package and the implications this might have for usability and product image. Drawings provided a quick, low-cost and effective means of exploring these issues but the team also used block models built out of rigid cellular foam to assess the styling of the product form.

Figure 10 Rigid cellular foam model of the DC05

You first came across a description of this material in the *Modelling Workbook* but you will also have seen its application in the DVD video sequence titled 'Philips: creative product design'. The foam is easily carved and shaped with simple tools. Components such as wheels are shaped separately and the whole lot assembled using glue. Foam models, such as that in Figure 10, usually present less ambiguity than might be the case with rendered elevations or perspective drawings of proposals. In this foam model the primary areas of interest were the form of the handles, the visual appearance and location of the switches and controls, and the overall visual detailing.

It is important to realise this process of form giving is not merely the shrouding of the underlying configuration of motor, piping and linkages. It is not merely a process of placing a skin over the muscle and skeletal frame of the cleaner. It is a process of interpretation requiring sensitivity to many conflicting influences, constraints and opportunities.

The process of giving a form and a visual identity to a product, and of visually linking or distinguishing components in a product, can make or break its success. It can directly influence buyers' perceptions and users' abilities to interact with it. As you saw from the studies of chairs in Block 1 external form can convey messages regarding, for example, where to hold or open the product; it can suggest a family identity with other Dyson products, and it might suggest qualities such as durability or robustness.

The foam model is not primarily concerned with the configurational aspects of the design such as the assembly of subsystems. These will have been fully explored via other modelling techniques. The foam model is essentially a means to assess ideas for visual form. It allows the design team to communicate with non-design staff who may not be able to interpret the limited visual information available in, say, a prototype or pages of sketch drawings and renderings. The foam model is dimensionally accurate although it does not represent the final surface texture or colour.

1.7 Rapid prototyping

Dyson Ltd has made vast financial investments in rapid-prototyping (RP) technologies and it is interesting to speculate on whether RP could have been used at the very early stages of this particular product. In principle, RP would have allowed the design team to model one or more components with one of the computer-aided design software systems and then to output this, straight from the computer, as a 3D form for incorporation into the prototype. In fact Dyson Ltd has three rapid-prototyping technologies in-house to do just this. It possesses systems for stereolithography addition (SLA), fusion deposition modelling (FDM) and selective laser sintering (SLS) (these techniques were discussed in Block 5).

However, this investment hasn't entirely eroded the need for technical staff. As you have already seen, many rapid-prototyping techniques produce components that have rough or stepped surfaces, particularly on curved surfaces, and these require a significant amount of hand finishing before they can be incorporated into models and prototypes. Also, skilled model makers can fashion visual or functional components with speed, accuracy and, most importantly, low cost. It's not always cost effective to have digital models made and converted into 3D form via RP technologies, especially at the concept stage when any number of variables might be changed or even the whole project cancelled.

Time spent developing CAD and RP models might be worthwhile in a number of circumstances, for example if the project concept was stable, if it was anticipated that several variations of a component might be necessary in development, or if assessment of the visual form mattered. The ability to use digital data to download slightly modified components would be superior to getting technicians to build new components from scratch every time. In the development of the DC05 the physical prototyping provided the data on which the CAD modelling was founded (discussed below).

Having noted the above limitations, I also speculate that as concept design increasingly incorporates digital modelling, and as computer-based techniques for testing and evaluating components and products improves, so there is likely to be less and less of the physical constructions that are so common in design practice today. Recent product development at Dyson confirms this trend. Nevertheless, many manufacturers still rely on the physical testing of prototypes to confirm that their products will perform in the marketplace. The art and science of the prototype builder is secure for the time being because even with digital modelling and rapid prototyping someone still has to assemble the 3D components into a working system.

In the case of the DC05 the model that emerged from the rapid-prototyping techniques was, in effect, close to the final design (Figure 11). It was the product as intended. There was nothing unexpected about the prototype that resulted from assembling the various RP components. All the design issues had been resolved via the drawings, the CAD models and the physical prototypes.

Figure 11 Rapid-prototype model in its near-final form

1.8 Testing products and prototypes

It has been known for members of the design staff to take prototypes home for a spot of domestic evaluation. While this is probably beneficial to the individual designer, and it certainly assists confidentiality, the testing strategy at Dyson is much more sophisticated. Dyson Ltd has an extensive product testing capability and this is exploited not only in product development but also in long-term trials as part of ongoing research and development. The company believes a comprehensive in-house testing facility is essential to long-term market success and it avoids the dangers of information leaking to competitors via third-party testing organisations.

Between 1992 and 2002 Dyson Ltd invested several million pounds in equipment to evaluate the performance of its products and much of this involved unique Dyson-designed test rigs (Figure 12). These include pneumatic rigs to repeatedly open and close a cleaner; a 'user course' where real users put machines through a range of tests that reproduce the cleaning problems found in typical households; rigs to rapidly simulate the stresses placed on the motors and the cyclone system; and numerous mechanical powered jigs to repeatedly drag the cleaner head across a piece of carpet, to repeatedly drop products in impact tests, and to assess wear in cables, hoses and linkages. Each of these test rigs is computer controlled and where possible the findings are collected by computer – for example, at which point a component fails.

In some cases qualitative judgements are required regarding the effect of the testing on the product. The findings are fed back to design so that the implications can be assessed and the necessary changes made. This might involve a change to a component form or it might mean a change of material specification or both.

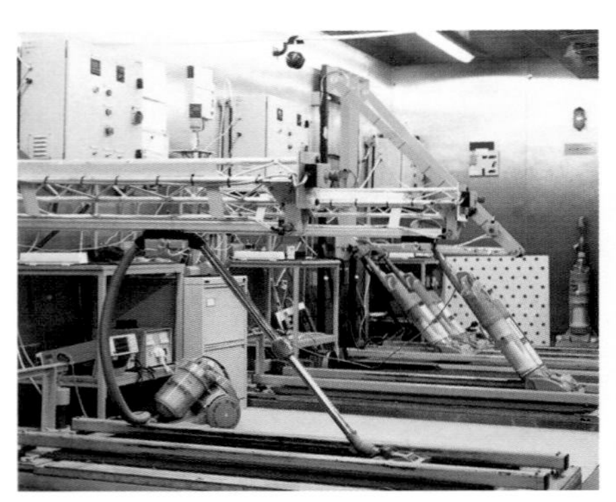

Figure 12 Rapid-life testing of the DC05 and other models

Figure 13 Drag testing on a rotating turntable

Abuse testing can be as important as testing products in normal or anticipated use. To achieve this the DC05 was placed in a test rig that repeatedly dragged it across a moving turntable so that the hose, shell and wheel mountings were subjected to fierce changes in direction, and various knocks and abrasion (Figure 13). Where such tests were conducted with rapid-prototyped components it was found these often failed in similar ways to the eventual real components and this gave confidence to the team to use RP technologies earlier in the process in future.

One of the purposes of testing is to ensure new products will conform to the appropriate standards and achieve the necessary approvals prior to launch. This is perhaps a less glamorous but essential aspect of design and development. If a manufacturer is found to be liable for an accident because of some design deficiency or fault with one of its products then the financial consequences could be immense in terms of fines, lost sales and wasted development costs.

There are all manner of international specifications, concerning, for example, the mechanical and electrical systems, to which products must conform. Each may result from a different testing authority and ensuring a product conforms to all the current and anticipated legislation can be complicated and time-consuming.

1.9 Production development

More than £1 million was committed to the tooling and other capital requirements necessary for the production of the DC05 in the UK but in 2002 production was switched to Asia. The first moulded samples came off the tooling in 1999 and a batch of DC05s was assembled. This first batch, referred to as T1s, was used to check the tolerances against those specified in the database and the drawings, to prove the fit between components, and to ensure accurate assembly (see Figure 14).

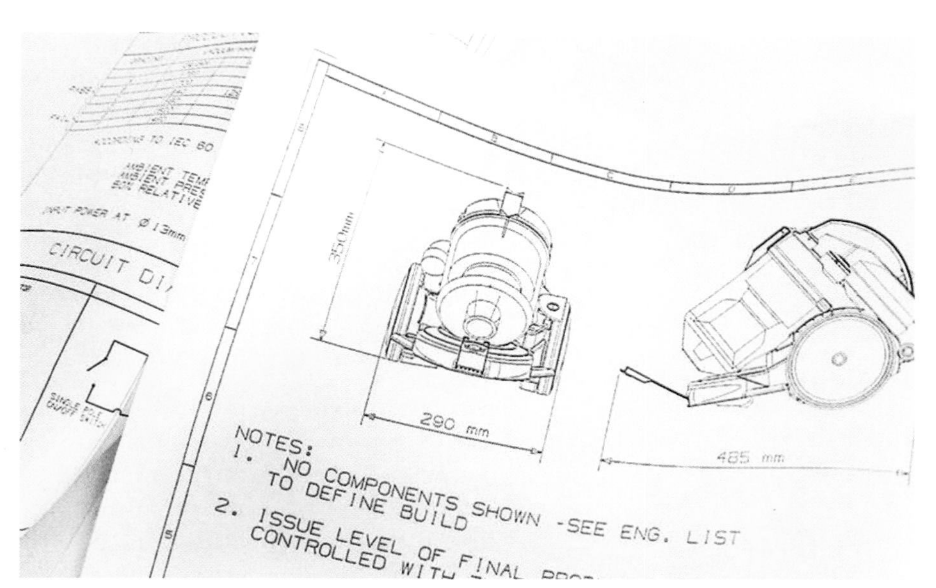

Figure 14 Drawings printed out from the DC05 database

1.9.1 Changing the colour of mouldings

As you saw in Block 5 changes to the colour of plastic mouldings can subtly alter their characteristics, including the ability to fit with other mouldings or components. Adding a different colour pigment can give rise to slightly different moulding characteristics, for example flow or cooling, or performance characteristics such as flexibility. A moulding in grey that produces a clear and positive click when snapped into place in the assembly might not do so when moulded in purple or green. The difference might be as small as 0.1 mm but it can affect the fit and, just as importantly, it can influence users' perceptions of the quality of the product.

This is significant with Dyson products because the company exploits strong contrasts in colour to achieve a distinct product identity across the whole range. This effect of colour pigment affecting component size is difficult to predict therefore the company built and evaluated the batch of T1s before the main production began.

1.9.2 Modifying the moulding tools

The T1s, the preproduction builds, also allowed production engineers to check the operation and performance of machines that would be expensive to stop once production was underway. This first batch of products was subjected to extensive testing in the rigs described above. Understandably there were small modifications to be made to the tooling. In fact every component required at least one modification to be made to the mould and in some cases up to six changes had to be made. This doesn't necessarily indicate errors or carelessness – toolmakers expect to make changes and the changes can often be made quite quickly.

In many instances mould tools will be made with a small excess of material so that it can be gradually pared back to provide the exact tolerance as determined via building and testing products. This is a much less difficult process than adding material to a mould tool.

Injection moulding tools are made from steel and for a big component, or where multiple components are made simultaneously, they can weigh several tons. Such tools can be very expensive – the injection mould tool for the main body of the Dyson DC04 cost around half a million pounds. From the tool the company would expect to get over one million mouldings before wear meant the tolerances were exceeded and the mould needed remaking.

Getting the tooling correct can be a nervous time for the project development team. The engineering drawings are signed off and there's no going back.

The time to make or modify plastics moulding tools can be a source of serious concern in the launch of a new product. Traditionally it can take up to 16 weeks to get a large injection mould tool made in the UK but new procedures pioneered in the rapidly expanding economies of south-east Asian countries such as Korea have resulted in major reductions in time and cost.

With reliable systems for electronic communication and data transfer now available, computer-aided design and computer-aided manufacture (CADCAM) has truly gone international. Many companies are turning to China and other countries in Asia for their tooling. However, security of intellectual property, especially where an innovative or new product is involved, is likely to remain a concern for the originators of the design.

1.9.3 Relocating manufacturing base

As wage levels are so much lower it is perhaps understandable that companies will move not only their tooling production but also their whole manufacturing base to these countries. In fact Dyson Ltd transferred its manufacturing activity from Wiltshire to Malaysia in 2002 for this very reason. For the DC05 Dyson used toolmakers in

Portugal and the UK. It remains to be seen whether the UK engineering firms can match the services and costs offered by overseas competitors so as to enable manufacturing companies to retain UK bases.

The development of the DC05 took place in the late 1990s, well before production at Dyson moved abroad, and a close link between design and production was visible. A second batch of components was produced four weeks after the T1s allowing T2s to be assembled and tested for final product validation. Efficient manufacturing required that the production staff underwent a period of training. They had to become familiar with the particular production requirements associated with particular processes or components and they had to become familiar with a totally new product in the Dyson range. This familiarity was achieved during a preproduction run before full production began (Figure 15).

Figure 15 DC05 products on the production line

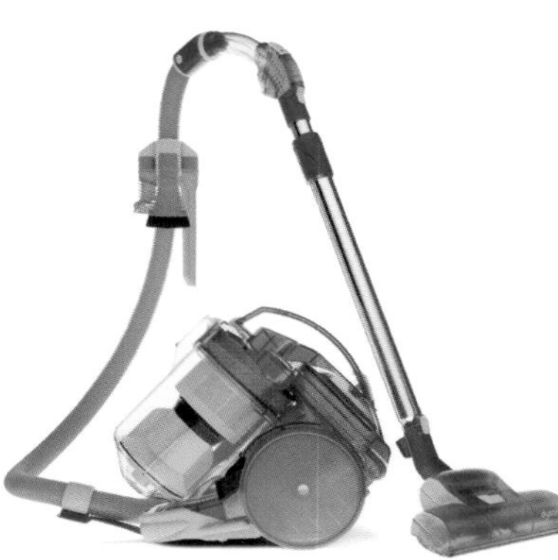

Figure 16 Two variations of the DCO5

With the start of production proper the engineering design team moved into a supporting position. Its role became one of troubleshooting, being immediately available to support production personnel if problems should arise. It might mean tracing back an assembly problem to a particular mould tool or helping to overcome an unexpected consequence of an earlier design modification. The engineering design team also became involved in the development of variations of the DC05 (Figure 16).

1.10 Endnote

This case study has provided an insight to a 15-month design and development programme at Dyson Ltd. The concept had emerged three months into the project and after six months detailed CAD models of all components had been made. At nine months the tooling was in development and early component parts were available for assembling into trial products. By the time the project had reached the end of its fifteenth month most of the production problems had been ironed out and the design team was able to move into a production support role, troubleshooting any emerging problems.

Dyson Ltd has created a strong reputation for design and innovation. Partly this is because its products have been technically innovative and partly because they have a strong image. Also, the company has a charismatic figurehead in James Dyson to champion the brand.

Less apparent is the significant investment in manufacturing systems and resources that James Dyson felt he needed to be internationally competitive. Some features of the organisation and its management are borrowed from overseas competitors, particularly Japanese companies that have for decades led the world in manufacturing systems. In spite of this, manufacturing in the UK has proved too costly and has been moved overseas. However, Dyson Ltd retains a significant workforce at the Malmesbury site. In addition to design and development there are departments for finance, logistics, purchasing, human resources, graphics, microbiology and testing, and a call centre.

2 Case study 2 Roller coaster design

2.1 Introduction

Figure 17 John Wardley, roller coaster designer

In March 2002, in a *Sunday Times* article titled 'Rides of your life', Mark Hodson postulated that John Wardley can perhaps be considered 'to have single-handedly transformed Britain's leisure parks from rattling end-of-the-pier amusements into international attractions'. What makes John Wardley (Figure 17) so relevant for study in this course is that, as a consultant director of the Tussauds Group, he is responsible for much of the design at some of the UK's leading leisure parks. He has done work for Alton Towers in Staffordshire, and Thorpe Park and Chessington World of Adventures, both located to the south west of London.

Wardley's background in stage illusions and the film industry – he created the special effects for five of the James Bond films – equips him with a deep understanding of what entertains the British public, together with a technical expertise to assess what is practical, safe, reliable and cost effective.

Wardley's designs for roller coasters are known and respected around the world. He designed Nemesis and Oblivion – the world's first vertical drop roller coaster – for Alton Towers and more recently has been responsible for the flying coaster Air (Figure 18) at the same park. He designed Colossus (Figure 19), a record-breaking 10-inversion coaster, and Nemesis Inferno for Thorpe Park, and further attractions are in development.

Figure 18 Air at Alton Towers

Figure 19 Colossus at Thorpe Park

There are a number of photographs of Wardley's rides included here but there is also a video sequence on the DVD showing some of the rides in action. Watch this video sequence at any point that is convenient to you.

2.1.1 Parks and rides

Before I turn to the case study proper I should define a few of the terms that appear. Let me begin by drawing a distinction between amusement parks and theme parks.

An amusement park uses many different devices to entertain visitors but they usually include roller coasters (or simply 'coasters'). Once these were simple open carriages guided by some form of rails around a tight circuit of sharp curves and steep descents but modern roller coasters are far from the traditional image of trains. Each ride has its own individual characteristics.

A theme park seeks to link its entertainment devices together as a story might link its characters together. It may or may not include coasters but whatever attractions it presents they are dressed to fit in with the theme or themes. Theme parks also usually display a greater investment in landscaping of the park environment. They exploit architecture, lighting, sounds and even smell to create the illusion that the customer is in a particular 'world'.

Rides in amusement parks tend to focus on the physical experience; those in theme parks tend to focus on the emotional experience. Of course any given park may contain elements of both making them hard to classify. Many theme parks include dark rides, which are rides constructed inside a closed internal environment that makes the staging and lighting of a story or experience that much easier. More recent developments include motion simulators, which are static platforms that present the physical and visual illusion of dramatic movement. Some of the most recent rides have combined motion simulators and roller coasters to produce dramatic multisensory experiences but, understandably, these can be the most expensive to produce and maintain.

2.1.2 Wooden and steel coasters

There are essentially two types of roller coasters, steel ones and wooden ones. Steel coasters offer the potential for faster, smoother rides. Most modern rides are of this type because they can be made to perform inverted manoeuvres such as loops and corkscrews that many visitors demand. Generally, wooden coasters or 'woodies' are slower, bumpier and do not loop. The first wooden coasters date back to the 1850s and there are many twentieth century examples still running. Modern woodies deliberately evoke the nostalgia of a bygone age and they can be just as exhilarating to ride as steel coasters. Part of this case study is devoted to the early design stages of a new wooden coaster planned to open at Alton Towers in 2006.

2.2 Modern roller coaster design

I arranged to meet with John Wardley early in 2003 to discuss his designs and his designing. I have woven into this study some quotations from our meeting at Alton Towers. But I want to open with an extended extract from a lecture John Wardley gave in 1994. It introduces many of the key issues in roller coaster design and it provided useful material around which I based my questions in 2003. As you read this study, look out for changes in John Wardley's design process between 1994 and 2003.

Modern roller coaster design

by John Wardley

Ask anyone who knows anything about roller coasters what is the one thing that has enabled the amazing developments in recent years in coaster technology, and they will almost certainly say computers.

It's a simple answer, and one that applies equally well to developments in virtually all other industries. But the computer is little more than a huge calculator that can manipulate numbers. What is it about numbers that enable today's coaster designers to do more daring things, in both wood and steel, safely?

Some 20 years ago, the late Len Smith of Barry Island was reminiscing to me on the building of the Scenic Railway at Great Yarmouth. Len recalled a German colleague who was supervising construction, and he said, 'Herr Heydrich would rope me to one of the roller coaster bogeys, and would send me off down a dip. If I made it up the other side, we would carry on building the next section of track. If I didn't, we would lower the next hill a foot or two, and we would try again'.

And that was how things were done. Everything relied on experience, craftsmanship and intuition. They'd try something a few inches higher or lower. Bank a bend a few more degrees and see what it looked like. Strengthen a chassis with a bit of angle-iron where it had cracked last season. Ah, those were the days.

But today, coaster designers have a quantitative grasp of how materials perform under stress and strain. The various energy-absorbing forces that slow down a coaster train – the friction in the wheel bearings, the rolling resistance of the wheels on the track, the air resistance on the train – can be calculated and predicted under all operating conditions. The days of trial and error are, thankfully, gone forever.

But why 'thankfully'? What fun it is to try something, and see if it works. If it does, great. If it doesn't, then think again. Some things can still be designed in that way – a new recipe by a chef, or a painting by an artist, for example – but not roller coasters. Materials are expensive, time is expensive, and today we consider people's lives and safety as priceless.

The roller coaster designer of today can not only calculate precisely how a ride will perform dynamically before a single piece of track is constructed (and do away with the need to rope the apprentice to a bogey), he can also check the stresses and strains on the track and structure. This ensures that it will support the loads imposed on it by the train, how it will fatigue, how it might degrade and how it will perform under extremes of wind or temperature or earthquake. And all this is thanks to numbers being manipulated quickly and effortlessly by computers.

Figure 20 Nemesis at Alton Towers

Not long ago at Alton Towers I waited nervously as the first train was to be sent around Nemesis, the inverter roller coaster that was engineered by the Swiss company Bolliger & Mabillard (Figure 20). For two years, layout and profile drawings had been sent back and forth between Walter Bolliger in Switzerland and my office in Wales. At last this £10 million giant was about to prove itself. Claude Mabillard was commissioning engineer on site, and the dispatch button was about to be pressed for the first time.

'What if it stalls?' and, 'How do we get it back into the station?' I asked Claude in trepidation. With a Gallic smile he replied quite simply, 'It won't stall. Our coasters never stall. Our coasters always work first time.'

And I could tell, he really meant it. He had no doubt whatsoever that he and his colleagues had done their calculations to perfection. The button was pressed and the massive train climbed the lift, and, yes, it did run perfectly first time to exactly the calculated specification.

So with total certainty of final performance, a roller coaster designer of today can let his creative imaginations blossom in the drawing office rather than by trial and error on site.

So how do I set about designing a roller coaster?

Design brief

It all starts with the marketeers. They need a new ride for their park, and they bombard you with statistics and jargon. Perhaps they want the highest in the world, perhaps they want the longest, and perhaps they want the scariest. They might want a heavily themed coaster, or a traditional wooden coaster. Or something high-tech and impressive. Or perhaps a good, family fun ride. Sometimes they haven't a clue what they want although they never admit it, and give you all the market research and leave you to come up with ideas. Sometimes they know exactly where it is to be located on the park, but more usually they say:

'Fit a coaster in the park where:

1 it can't be seen from outside the park (note to our American friends: we in England have zoning restrictions that force us to hide our coasters in our parks, whereas you in the States can proudly show them off to everyone in the surrounding county, or even the state);
2 it will draw people away from the main entrance and towards the back of the park;
3 it won't require any trees to be felled;
4 it will fit in with an existing themed area.'

Location and planning consent

Perhaps the single most influential factor in coaster design at our parks in England (Alton Towers, Thorpe Park and Chessington World of Adventures) is that of obtaining planning consent. We might know exactly what type of coaster we want, we might know exactly where we would like to put it, we might even have the money ready to build it, but without planning consent we might as well forget it. So instead, we talk to the local planners and establish some basic ground rules before submitting planning applications. This is an issue we can never expect roller coaster enthusiasts to understand. They are frustrated by the fact we have the site, we have the technology, we have the customers, and we have the money, so why don't we stop hanging around and get on and build their dream coaster. If only it was as simple as that.

Once I have the location and site boundaries agreed we do a balloon test to ascertain the maximum heights at various points around the site where the structure can reach. This simply consists of flying helium-filled balloons on strings to various heights at key points around the site, and photographing them from contentious vantage points around the locality. If a balloon can be seen by anyone, anywhere, off-site it's back to the drawing board. Now perhaps you can understand the enormous restrictions that are imposed upon us when designing our coasters.

I then consider the ride in the perspective of the whole park (see Figure 21). How is it to be approached, and from which directions? How visible will it be on approach? Where should the station be, what other buildings are to be included in the development (shops, restaurants, toilets).

Figure 21 Map of Alton Towers park

Layout

Normally, wherever the local planners have determined the highest point of the structure can be, this fixes the position of the top of the lift, which is the mechanism that raises the cars at the start of a ride. We draw a straight line on the plan back from this high point roughly in the direction of where the station is to be and sufficiently long for the lift. When we draw the line we try to avoid existing trees and other obstructions and that fixes the position of the lift hill. Next, we take a line back from the base of the lift (through a bend if necessary) and create the line of the station, transfer table (for switching cars from the main track to sidings) and safety brakes, preferably all in a straight line.

I say preferably because I broke this rule once on the Vampire at Chessington World of Adventures, and I regret it. Because of the awkward space available for the station on this ride – a suspended coaster made by Arrow – there had to be a 180-degree bend between the brakes and the station. Naturally, the train cruised round this bend at a relatively slow speed, having already been braked for the station, and valuable time was lost resulting in a loss of capacity of around 4 per cent of the total hourly capacity of 1650 customers per hour.

From these decisions the position of the train storage tracks can be decided. And we still haven't designed the runaway yet. The runaway is the section of track from the top of the lift, back into the safety brakes – excluding any block brakes or slowers. This is where the fun starts, but it is not as easy as you might think. Firstly, we have to remember Sir Isaac Newton. The lift imparts potential energy into the train, and the track, wheel bearings and air resistance take it away. The motion of the train is a constant juggling exercise converting potential energy into kinetic energy, and back again, while gradually subtracting frictional energy losses.

Figure 22 Extreme vertical drop on Oblivion

Perhaps the element you think is the most important is the *first drop* (Figure 22). In theory this is potentially the most exciting element, because the train starts at the highest point of the ride, and can go down to the lowest if the top of the lift is somewhere near the lowest point of the site. But any fool can design a good first drop on a ride. All you have to do is decide whether you want a straight drop or a twisting drop. I prefer a straight drop, because it gives that true free-falling sensation, but that is only personal preference. But ask yourself the question, 'Should the first drop be the best?'

A roller coaster is designed to *entertain*. Think about other forms of entertainment. Why does a circus trapeze artist leave his most daring trick to the end? Why is the most thrilling scene in a movie left to the end? Most forms of entertainment build up to a climax, whereas roller coasters, because of the laws of gravity, tend to get more and more feeble as they get towards the end. And this is where the designer's skill comes in.

A well-designed roller coaster keeps the thrills and fun going right up to the station brakes. The real classic coasters all do this … Beast at Kings Island, Revolution at Magic Mountain, Grand National at Blackpool, Thunderbolt at Kennywood to name but four. The bad coasters, and I won't name them, start brilliantly but then get more and more dull and slow and boring as they reach the station. And that is not what entertainment is all about.

So I don't tend to throw everything into the first drop. I like to keep a little back, so that the rest of the ride is fun, with plenty of surprises. A roller coaster is a total adventure, and it is a great pity when the quality of that adventure is compromised by the need to get into the record books with the highest first drop, the fastest first drop, the steepest first drop, and so on. Often, the quality of the rest of the ride suffers as a result.

The location and orientation of the first drop is also important if the ride is to look impressive to outside observers. Where a coaster is being used to draw people onto a whole park, the view of that first drop from off the park is crucial. As with Pepsi Max at Blackpool, the sight of that enormous drop from Blackpool promenade is very impressive. Come to think of it, the sight of it from almost everywhere else in Lancashire is impressive.

The basic brief I am given for the ride will determine many of the characteristics of the rest of the layout. Is it to be a rough thriller or a smooth family charmer; steep or gentle drops; perfect banking or jerky bends; tunnels and hidden surprises or all up front?

Plan and profile

The technique of designing the track relies on amalgamating two separate devices: the *plan* and the *profile*. The plan speaks for itself. It is a line on the ground directly beneath the track. It fixes the layout in the horizontal plane, and is the line you would see if you viewed the coaster from directly overhead. The profile is the line of the track in space, as if viewed from the side, but with the layout unwound as if the track were all in one straight continuous line. It looks rather like a long graph, with the base line (the horizontal axis) representing either the lowest point of the site, the lowest point of the track, or some arbitrary Ordnance Survey datum level. The vertical axis represents the height above the base line. The profile fixes the layout in the vertical plane [shown later in Figure 24].

If you draw the profile onto a piece of card and cut it out, you can then bend this around and stand it up on the plan to give you a crude three-dimensional model of the ride. It is this model-making process that an experienced coaster designer can do in his mind, creating a three-dimensional composite picture of the ride in his imagination from the two elements of the plan and profile.

I first draw a plan, keeping in the back of my mind the lengths required for typical dips from given heights. I then mark a few spot heights on this plan, and use these to draw a profile. From this first profile a number of problems will arise.

1. Crossovers. Often tracks will try to cross over at similar levels and will collide.
2. Gradients too steep or too shallow. The profile should look like a series of smooth, sensuous undulations.
3. Dynamics look wrong. It will be apparent from a look at the profile if the train will not make the next hill. The profile must have a steady average downhill gradient.

A new plan is drawn up, taking account of the problems the first profile has highlighted. More spot heights are put on this amended plan, and a second profile is drawn up. This process is repeated over and over again until the ride appears right in both the horizontal and vertical planes. This is then given to the chosen manufacturer to check out the dynamics of the ride and make sure the train will roll at a safe and satisfactory speed all around the circuit. A check is made to ensure the train will come back into the station with sufficient energy to make the end of the ride exhilarating, but not too much energy to have to dissipate in the brakes.

Capacity

Once a basic layout and profile has been agreed, this has to be turned into a practical working machine that will have sufficient capacity for the demands of the operation. The capacity of the ride, normally expressed in passengers per hour, is a function of the theoretical capacity of the individual trains, the efficiency of filling the trains to capacity, and the rate at which those trains can be dispatched. The rate at which the trains can be dispatched is determined by the track ahead, the train availability, and the speed of loading.

If there is only one train on the track, the track ahead is always clear, and the rate of dispatch is the total circuit time plus loading-unloading time. However, when more than one train is on the track at any one time, the circuit is divided into a series of safety blocks, where a set of closed brakes, or the lift itself, must separate any two trains on the circuit. Having calculated the capacity the ride can give with one train, if it is decided a second train (or more) is necessary to give the required capacity, then the circuit needs to have safety blocks designed into it. If the main runaway section is so long that it is necessary to have more than one train in the runaway at any one time, then a set of safety brakes must be inserted into the circuit. These must normally be located on a straight section of track, and it is these brakes enthusiasts hate.

The reason why they – or should I say we, because I'm as big an enthusiast as any other – hate them is they are usually permanently applied to slow the trains down, even if the block ahead is clear. But why? If the block ahead is clear, why can't the trains whiz straight through them? Why are they also applied as slowers or check brakes?

Well, think about it for a moment ... Supposing something goes wrong and a train has to stop temporarily in these block brakes somewhere halfway round the circuit. When the block ahead clears, it is necessary to open the block brakes, and the train must coast from a standing start safely around the rest of the circuit without stalling. Now, if the circuit is designed for a train to leave the block brakes from a standing start, it is therefore not designed for a train to leave the block brakes at full running speed, where it will belt round the rest of the circuit with an excess of kinetic energy. If the circuit is designed for the train to leave the block brakes at full running speed, the chances are that if it leaves them from a standing start it won't make the next hill, and will stall.

This is why I do everything I can to not have block brakes in the runaway sections of my rides. The only way around the problem would be to have accelerators that launch a stopped train out of the block brakes, to replace the energy that the brakes took out of the train when it brought it to a halt.

With more than one train on the circuit, a means of switching trains on and off the track is necessary, and that is where the transfer table and storage tracks are needed. In some cases the designs are very simple and manually operated – watching the operators shunt trains on the old woodies is a joy to behold. In others, the mechanisms are fully automatic, but equally intriguing. If you can, get to Alton Towers early in the morning, and watch the Nemesis trains silently and automatically gliding themselves onto the main circuit. It's quite spooky.

Operation

The speed of loading of the train affects capacity, and the quicker people can load and unload in the station, the shorter the queues. This is why a well-designed station is essential to the efficient operation of a roller coaster. Some features are obvious, such as the preloading of the next train in a series of loading 'chutes', often with automatic gates. But there are many other less obvious features you may have never considered.

Traditionally, most roller coasters loaded and unloaded at separate points on the platform. The train would enter the station, stop and unload, then pull forward and stop again to load. This was time consuming. Now most coasters are designed to load and unload in one bite, unloading on one side, and, after a brief pause, loading on the other. It is interesting to note that many old woodies are being converted to one-bite operation.

I always try to ensure that on all my rides wherever possible the queue enters the station at a slightly elevated level, so that the arriving visitors look down on the loading platform and immediately become orientated and acquainted with what is expected of them in the next few minutes. The point at which these ramps discharge onto the platform freeway behind the chutes is also important. Given a choice, most people's first preference would be to sit at the front of the train, and their second preference would be to sit at the back. As I'm sure you'll appreciate, if we allowed everyone to sit just where they wanted, the trains would go out half empty, and the queue would hardly move. So the queue is allowed to flood the freeway behind the chutes roughly one-third up the platform from the back, or two-thirds down from the front, and this tends to assist in filling up all the chutes to near capacity.

At pay-one-price parks, queues for all major rides can get enormous. Waiting times for big coasters can get as long as two or three hours. Imaginatively designed queue lines are therefore very important.

American parks tend to go for zigzag cattle pen queue lines. The advantage of these is you can get a lot of people into a small space, and can shade them from the heat of the sun with a roof. But Europeans don't like being penned up like this, and are much happier in a well-landscaped meandering queue path, with much to see at every twist and turn.

Themes and landscaping

Landscaping around a coaster can be important, whether the coaster is themed or not. Mature landscaping can be a great asset, although designing a coaster around existing trees is difficult. The whole setting in which a coaster is located improves the ride itself, the waiting for the ride, and the view of the ride for outside observers. Themeing and special effects, both on the station and around the circuit, can add an extra dimension to the ride. Apparent obstacles in the path of the train such as tunnels and waterfalls create fun and added excitement.

So much for the physical ride. But the designer has much more to do.

Name and image

Traditionally, a coaster would be given a dynamic, emotive name (Thunderbolt, Giant Racer, Cyclone, and such like) and the park's marketing department would be told to get on and promote it. And they would invariably use as much hype as possible, relying on words such as highest, fastest, meanest, scariest, and so on to be the main promotional come-on. Such coasters are known as abstract themed coasters.

In the seventies, parks started notionally themeing their coasters, and gave them names that fired the visitors' imaginations (Python, Loch Ness Monster, Iron Dragon, and so on). A much more imaginative approach could therefore be taken to the decoration of the ride station, the logo and signs, the souvenir merchandise and the TV commercials.

Although in modern times we tend to assume Disney led the way with fully themed coasters, (first with Matterhorn at Disneyland, then Space Mountain, then Big Thunder Railroad), in fact as early as 1910 LaMarcus Thompson built a huge scenic railroad next to Venice Pier in California, complete with mountainous scenery. Full themeing takes the coaster into a whole new spectrum, which many enthusiasts and purists say is unnecessary because the actual ride is little more than a transit system that is used to explore or negotiate a themed environment. But such rides are responsible for winning many new coaster enthusiasts, who would not have normally ridden a large coaster if it had been abstract and unthemed.

If the theme, name, logo and image of a coaster are strong enough, it can actually become a marketable property in its own right. In the past, coasters have bought existing intellectual property rights such as Batman, Top Gun and others, or have been sponsored by established products, for example Pepsi Max. Nemesis turned all this upside down, with Coca-Cola actually manufacturing a Nemesis drink, and a CD of the musical soundtrack going on release. The strength of the Nemesis brand created such national sales – in shops around Britain, not only on the park – that the Nemesis drink sold out the first production run of 1.2 million cans in the first six weeks, with a second production run of 2.4 million cans immediately following. Each can sold earned Alton Towers money from license royalties.

On-park merchandise linked with the ride must be designed and ordered – often up to nine months before the ride opens, to allow for manufacturing and delivery times. The sale of souvenir merchandise not only brings additional revenue to the park, but also helps to promote the ride off-park.

Promotion and advertising

You would think once the coaster has been built, the designer has finished his task. Not so. If the promotion of the attraction is to be maximised, the design philosophies that went into its creation have to follow through into its promotion.

Perhaps the biggest headache I always get in the lead-up to the opening of a new ride is the filming of the TV commercial.

The marketing people always say they need this on the nation's TV screens a few days before the official opening, which means it has to be filmed about two months in advance. But invariably the ride is still being built at this time, and even if it is running, the site looks like a construction site with piles of muck and scaffolding everywhere. So the week of the filming is always very traumatic, with people disguising piles of rubbish, and generally faking everything up so that on the screen the ride looks magnificent.

Then I get wheeled around doing interviews ... radio, TV, newspapers ... *Blue Peter*, *Big Breakfast*, *Tomorrow's World*, *Daily Express*, the *Sun*, Radio Johannesburg ... I'm filmed on the ride, under it, and over it. I talk about the technicalities of designing it, about the problems of building it, and the thrills and horrors of riding it. I talk about how I thought up the idea in the first place, and they ask me what I'm going to design next. And each time I seem to be saying exactly the same thing, over and over again.

Then the great day comes. The grand opening. And what should be a most wonderful and exhilarating day for me is usually dreadfully depressing. Why? Because I have to hand over my baby to someone else to bring up. Other people now take control. It is no longer mine. But always in the back of my mind is the next one ... that bit better, more exciting, more entertaining.

(John Wardley, 13 June 1994)

2.3 Beginning of design – information and creativity

I met with John Wardley at Alton Towers in February 2003. I was keen to explore his involvement in the planning stages of a new design project, his creative development of new concepts and his working relationship with the manufacturers during the detail design process. Clearly, computer-aided design had moved on since the 1994 lecture and I was keen to explore how this had influenced Wardley's design process.

2.3.1 Site surveys

Large engineering projects such as a theme park ride rely on accurate data about the intended site. This includes a site survey of the topography of the land and its features. The design team have an archive of paper charts at their disposal as well as an electronic database (Figure 23). John Wardley called up a recent Alton Towers site survey on his laptop computer and this clearly showed the location of Nemesis and Air and all the other rides. It defined the boundaries to the park, the gardens, buildings and other constructed landmarks as well as natural features such as trees and the main valley that runs north-west to south-east at Alton Towers.

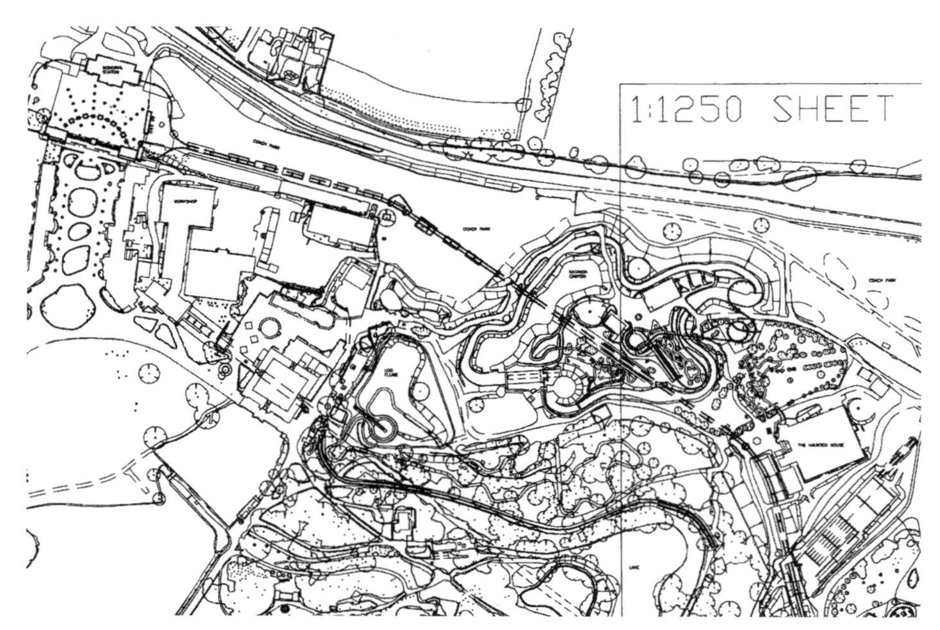

Figure 23 Part of a detailed plan of the Alton Towers park

The site survey can be used to present the viewer with the ground plan – rather like a detailed contour map, and it can be used to generate sections – as if the site could be seen from any number of imaginary side views. Even the heights of the trees are accurately recorded. These views of the skyline are vital if the proposed rides are to conform to the many regulations imposed by the planning authorities.

Here's an excerpt of John Wardley talking about the site survey of Alton Towers. The discussion concerned a proposal to design and build a major new wooden roller coaster at Alton Towers that will run from one side of the site to the other and exploit the natural valley to accelerate the riders. It provides an insight into that joint process of problem exploration and idea generation.

> There's woodland here that contains the old stone quarries from which the original Alton Towers house was built. We are talking about taking the ride from this side, down the valley, up the other side and round the back. You can see all the trees are plotted. I know, for example, that this tree is 14 metres high and immediately I get a feeling for the sorts of heights that we can probably go to in the new design. In my mind I start to shape up an idea. One idea would be to have a station here, the cars would rise to a height of about 20 metres above the ground, there would be a few dips and then a massive dip right down to the bottom and up the other side. By this point the train wouldn't have enough energy to return so I've put in a second lift that takes riders up, then down and back up the other side.

Wardley's process involves extended exposure to the site by walking over the terrain and then sitting down with the plans and profiles and other computer-based data. When a design concept emerges that seems to match the restrictions and opportunities of the site a number of different types of model are used to develop and evaluate such ideas. One such model, existing only on the laptop computer, is simply an unwound version of the idea. The computer can be used to present proposals as if they existed in a straight line – showing the profile of the ground as one coloured line, a notional tree canopy height at around 20 metres above this and, between the two, a third line representing the profile of the track (Figure 24).

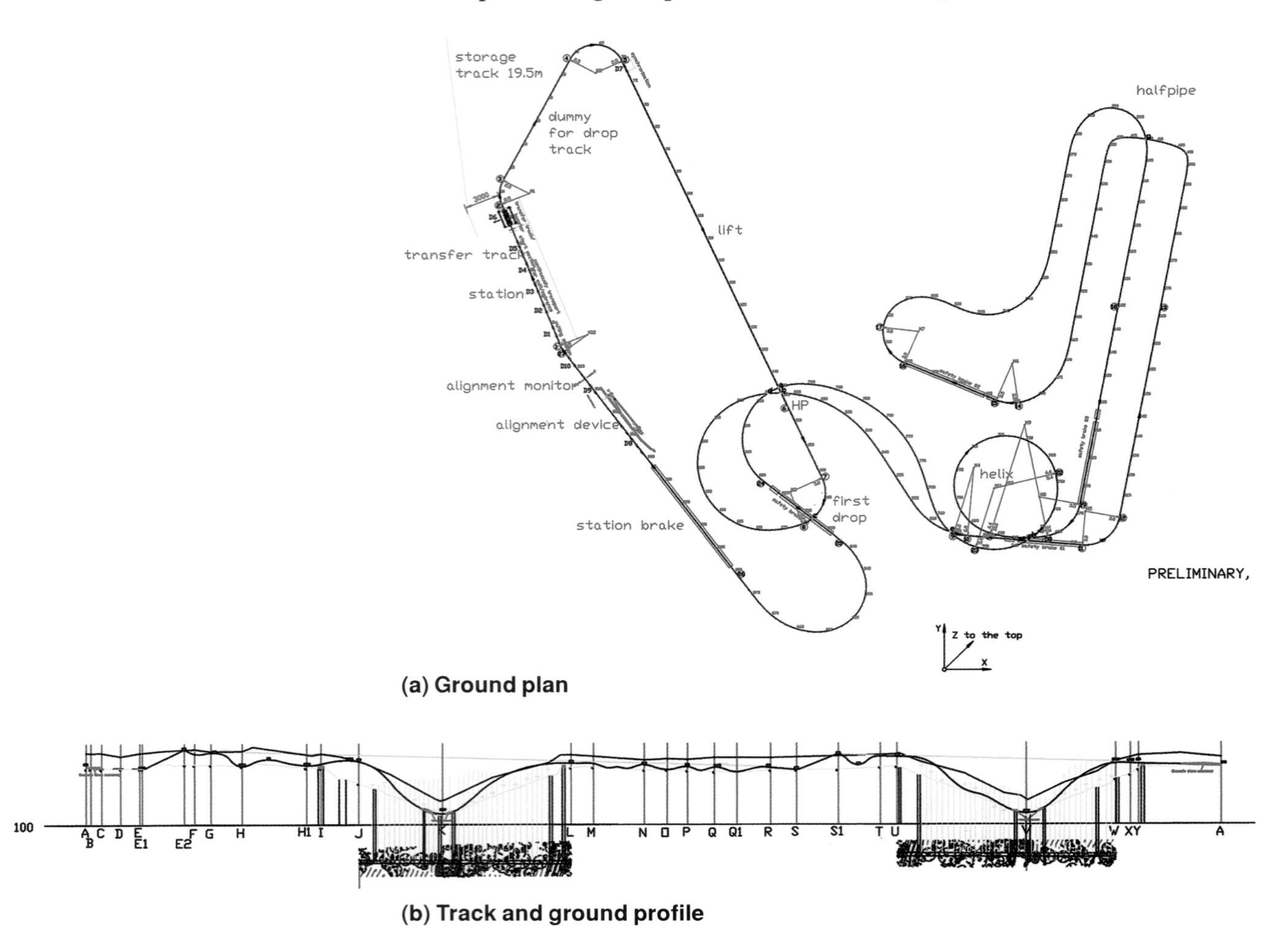

(a) Ground plan

(b) Track and ground profile

Figure 24 Concept design represented as plan and profile

As you saw in John Wardley's 1994 lecture, local planning restrictions dictate that rides must not project above the tree canopy, but being creative within constraints is a normal, day-to-day demand for designers. When he designed Oblivion, which opened at Alton Towers in 1998, Wardley got around this restriction by burying part of the ride in the ground. Not only does this keep the overall height of the ride below the tree canopy but also it allows riders to experience a dramatic descent into a cavernous hole thereby creating a unique characteristic to the ride. These characteristics are valuable to the marketing of rides and are significant to what people remember about the experience and recommend to their friends. In this case he took a potential problem (a limit on the height of the ride) and converted it into a positive characteristic (the ride drops into a hole).

Can you think of any other examples of products highlighted in this course where a designer or design team was confronted by an apparent problem but turned this into a positive feature of the design?

Wardley's computer profile model is also able to provide feedback regarding the energy in the cars at any point. The model can show the average gradient between the top of a lift and the station, or any places where the cars might be brought to a standstill such as at braking points. Each type of roller coaster will have its own characteristics for energy loss so it is possible to identify where modifications to the track need to be made. The computer model allows representations of the cars to travel along the profile to check they are able to make it to a station under all conditions. Of course, it is possible to add accelerators to increase the energy in the cars but this will increase overall build and running costs.

2.3.2 Developing the concept

Once an idea is worked up, and it seems to have potential, a number of other people become involved. It might be that one of the Alton Towers ecologists discovers there is a new badger set exactly where one of the foundations needs to be placed, causing a rethink to the track or its supports in that location. There are also certain trees that are completely protected while others are discovered to be rotten and need to come down. The design may need to accommodate both. The concept design stage is an iterative process, offering ideas based on the information available and then testing them out – both by computer modelling and by mapping it onto the real site. It results in concept designs that work – but at this stage, only in theory.

(The following quotations are by John Wardley unless otherwise stated.)

> Creativity is very much a team thing. Whereas when I started in this business many years ago ... it was definitely a one-man thing. Now we have a huge team of people here within the Tussauds Group. The 'think tank' of each of the parks – the core team – will chew around ideas. I will work with the art director at Tussauds studios and his team of designers. We will have brainstorming sessions and we will allow creative ideas to develop. It's no longer just me and my drawing board or my computer anymore.

The computer simulation is particularly useful for allowing others to share the vision of what any given proposal looks like. Very few people are able to look at plans and elevations and mentally construct an image of the proposal. Most people without some experience of design and designing need a bit of help in visualising ideas. Wardley uses a piece of software called No Limits that converts data about site, track profiles, shape, materials and brakes into a simulation as viewed from one of the cars. So a simulated ride can be tried before any work begins on site and before any significant funds are invested in the project. When run on a laptop computer it can be very convenient to take to early exploratory meetings about planning, funding or marketing.

Of course, the design will undergo a number of changes and there may be several different simulations produced. The simulation may suggest that certain sections of the ride can be made more dramatic or it may indicate that the speed of the cars needs to be modified, perhaps by changing the profile of a bend (Figure 25). Once planning consent has been granted and the layout and profile is finalised, the CAD model is remade so that it accurately represents every detail of the site and every detail of the proposed structure.

Figure 25 Achieving the twisting motion of Air was only possible with CAD modelling of the structures

I asked John Wardley whether he finds he now only needs to work with CAD or whether he still finds himself drawing and making card models.

> I used to take the plan and the profile, at some convenient scale, laminate the paper printout onto card and cut them out. I'd bend the profile around and stick it on the plan so that I created a three-dimensional representation of the ride. I would then get the design studio to convert this into a much more accurate three-dimensional model using plastic sections. It would have all sorts of other features added to the model such as buildings and trees. It was a very good way of allowing the whole team to talk about the operational issues of the proposal ranging from sight lines to where litter bins might go. Nowadays I don't have these detailed models built because I can do it all within the CAD programme. I find working with a layout and a profile and switching backwards and forwards is the finest way for me to be constantly aware of all the different obstructions and requirements.

2.4 Converting the concept into an engineered product

Once the layout and profile of a new ride have been agreed and all the necessary planning permissions have been obtained, the specification is sent out to selected companies so that they can develop a quotation for the detail design and construction. Sometimes these companies arrange to view the site or they might want to talk to John Wardley or other Alton Towers directors about particular aspects such as customer experience or the integration of the new ride with existing attractions.

> For the new wooden coaster we asked five companies to tender for the project but it is now down to a shortlist of two. In the case of a speciality roller coaster – perhaps one with a unique feature – there might be one manufacturer that specialises in that type of feature. In this case I would be working with that particular manufacturer right from the start. However, some manufacturers like to play around with the three-dimensional model too much. I want them to concentrate on the boring stuff like getting the thing to fit the site.

2.4.1 Developing the project team

Up to this point a roller coaster design project will have involved quite a small and intimate team around John Wardley, consisting of other directors at Alton Towers, planners and assistants, for example. Once a manufacturer is engaged the size of the team might increase considerably. The skills required at this stage are different. The project becomes a process of refinement. Different specialists contribute their own particular skill. You have seen that planning consultants have been involved from the earliest design stage. This ensures any investment in detail design will not be wasted simply because a design contravenes the planning regulations.

In order for the planners to give full consideration to the proposal they need to be provided with sections through the site showing, for example viewing points, off-site features and sight lines. Architects are normally involved at this stage to advise on and to produce these drawings. Alton Towers needs to secure funding for each new project and, in parallel with the planning application, there will be negotiations concerning the financial requirements.

At this stage a project team will be put together. Although John Wardley has a prominent position in the team, the Tussauds Group usually arranges its teams around a project champion who will normally be a senior executive from the particular theme park where the ride will be located. There would be the art director from Tussauds' studios who would be responsible for the styling and decoration of the attraction. It's usual to include someone from the park's engineering department, and there will be an architect, probably a civil engineer and maybe an electrical engineer depending on how complex the project is. Also there would be people in the team who are familiar with the local landscape and the estate itself. Additionally, there would be a marketing person and there would be someone representing the people who actually press the buttons and get visitors on and off the rides. Finally there would probably be a commercial manager concerned about merchandising and retail opportunities. It's quite a big team, containing perhaps 8–12 people and that's before any representatives from the selected manufacturer become involved.

2.4.2 Working with the manufacturer

Normally a manufacturer won't attend the early, formative project meetings largely because they are not appointed until later in the process. One team member, the group head of engineering, will have responsibility for liaison with selected manufacturers in order for them to produce their quotations against a written brief. In most cases this written brief will be a very detailed document – often running to 40–50 pages. Over and above this will be the contract determining and specifying the nature of the service. Given the detail in these two documents the activities of the manufacturer are fairly easy to predict.

In the case of some of the earlier world famous rides at Alton Towers, it was the manufacturer that defined the requirements for the foundations for each ride. The manufacturer determined the forces and loadings on these foundations and specified exactly where the fixings would be. It was the civil engineers at Alton Towers who converted these specifications into actual designs for the foundations and had them built on site. A delivery schedule is drawn up specifying the arrival dates of components but little of this routine level of activity needs to occupy the development team. However, there will be numerous on-site meetings involving many of these peripheral participants.

In the case of Air, Wardley and the team were working with one specific manufacturer because they had been working up the idea of a 'flying' coaster with this manufacturer for a number of years. The Tussauds Group works with two Swiss companies that are considered world leaders in this field – Bolliger & Mabillard (B&M) and Intamin. Both are independent companies, with international clients and produce rides of the highest levels of engineering quality and innovation. Air was developed with B&M so it doesn't represent the open-tender process used for other rides belonging to the Tussauds group.

> When there is only one manufacturer that can produce something for us then our board are prepared to let us go ahead providing we can justify it commercially. In the case of a coaster that any number of companies could produce, and where there probably wouldn't need to be much dialogue with the manufacturers, we formulate the brief and the planning profile and distribute this information to a number of manufacturers for them to respond. Those we want to shortlist we talk to and they will be invited back to make a presentation of design proposals and recommendations. Some projects are straightforward and the manufacturers can follow our brief closely. Other projects require more work on the part of the manufacturer. Once a manufacturer is appointed we will sit down with them and fine-tune the specification and the contract. In the case of a standard ride their job is really to make it work safely and reliably.

A significant amount of design takes place at this stage. Each manufacturer will have its preferred CAD modelling systems and each will engage in the prototyping of components and assemblies in order to further test proposals. The making of the CAD models of each component, the manufacture of each part, their combination as a prototype and their testing all add new information. These iterations between problem and solution are a key characteristic of design activity. Each model and each prototype is not merely a design proposal, an answer to a fixed problem; each can be a revealing insight to the *real* problem that must become the focus for creative thinking and problem solving.

Figure 26 Harness used to support the riders on the Air ride

Figure 27 Static harness for the Air ride, allowing the public to try the securing system

The rider's harness for Air was largely designed using full-size models. This unique harness allows the rider to begin in a sitting position but once the ride has started, a mechanism changes their orientation placing them with their backs uppermost in a horizontal 'flying' position (Figures 26 and 27).

> The first test rig was basically just a few bits of steel welded together with some seat mouldings from inverted coasters. And then gradually bits were added and rough foam shapes were cut in order to simulate the padding and so on. And gradually it was refined and matured and eventually a prototype vehicle was created from scratch. That was then used to take the patterns and moulds for the final product.

At one point in the development of this harness, the manufacturer toyed with the idea of building a dedicated centrifuge to experiment with the same forces that Air was to produce.

2.4.3 Funding of prototypes

Of course, not all roller coaster projects demand such a high level of innovation or require such sophisticated facilities for testing. A lot of roller coaster design is simple product refinement – making small, incremental changes. The basic running gear or the harness mechanism might be very similar to earlier designs with a potentially huge saving in development costs.

> As far as track is concerned there is rarely a need to build a prototype length. It would be far too expensive. Occasionally we might build a track test rig. Prototyping can be hugely expensive. For example, Intamin is now producing coasters powered by linear induction motors (LIMs). Intamin also produces hydraulically launched coasters. The main drawback with LIMs is their colossal demands on electrical power – it can be a couple of megawatts over 4–5 seconds. Working prototypes of these systems require serious investment. Similarly there have been ideas for rides that exploit a flywheel to store kinetic energy. To

> prototype such a device would be quite an undertaking. Intamin has come up with a very workable and realistic means of simulating its hydraulic launch systems using nitrogen-filled accumulators. These are charged to colossal pressures and then discharged so that hydraulic fluid is forced through an array of hydraulic motors around a huge winch drum that launches a train via a steel cable. Now, that is something they had to prototype full size. They didn't actually launch the train up 100 metres in the air but they nevertheless were able to launch the train at 80 miles an hour and into some kind of decelerating device.

And who, you might ask, picks up the tab for such expensive prototyping? It's usually the manufacturers simply because the various theme parks and amusement parks wouldn't pay for development that is not going to increase their own revenue. Probably the only entertainment organisation that is prepared and able to commit huge sums of money into research and development is Disney. Disney will not only fund the manufacture of rides but it has sophisticated information-gathering systems. It knows what it wants and funds manufacturers to conduct the necessary research and product development.

The Disney Corporation is innovative in all aspects of research and development but that doesn't stop it learning from the competition. Alton Towers pioneered the virtual queue system, allowing customers a 'fast track' to rides. Disney heard about it, sent a team over to Alton Towers for a week to watch it in action and negotiated a development deal. In this, Disney gained access to information that enabled it to conduct its own R&D and, in return, Alton Towers received a refined version of the system.

2.4.4 John Wardley's role

As you might expect, the detailing of a design usually requires many meetings. Sometimes these are full team meetings but more frequently they involve specific participants depending on whether the subject under discussion is the engineering, the planning, the finance or the marketing. John Wardley is often called upon to be present at these meetings. Sometimes the matter is routine engineering while other meetings are more stimulating.

> In the case of Air I was interested in the way the harnesses would actually work and I was keen to visit the factory to see the early tests. Many other aspects of the design are fully specified in the documentation and I'm very happy to leave them to create a product that performs as per the contract. These matters can easily be verified by our maintenance and engineering people.

As a consultant director with responsibility for concept design, Wardley's job is to maintain an overview of the whole project – not to get lost in the minutiae of mechanical or financial matters. His role brings him into contact with various specialist contributors to a project. He can act as a bridge between these contributors, knowing a little bit about everybody else's role so that the overall concept is maintained. He has to be certain in his own mind that the public will be safe, that the ride will be reliable and that downtime when the ride is not available for use is reduced to the minimum.

2.5 Safety and reliability

Safety is the number one priority in all matters concerning existing and new rides at Alton Towers. The following quote by John Wardley can be found on the course DVD.

> If you take a ride like Air we are potentially putting our guests in quite a perilous position ... We're strapping them into a harness face down and suspending them a long way above the ground and then we're turning them upside down and spinning them round and moving them around in a pretty dynamic way. In any other industries or activities where you're putting people in that sort of situation, such as hang gliding or parachuting, firstly you'd need to train the people ... and you would probably spend at least 10 or 15 minutes harnessing them up and checking and so on. Now in the theme park industry we have to take people of all shapes and sizes in huge numbers and very quickly get them harnessed up. In the case of Air we have to harness up about 28 people every 30 seconds ... You have to take somebody who hasn't got a clue what is going to happen to them, who is probably jumping up and down in excitement and is not seriously engaging their brain ... and almost automatically put them in a position where some kind of automatically adjusting harness clamps them into position and turns them face downwards such that they feel secure ... comfortable and ... safe to be lifted up and spun around ... without a seat or anything beneath them. The solution to that problem is probably one of the greatest triumphs to date of the amusement industry.

In the development of new rides huge safety margins are built into the designs as they are in ordinary kinds of public transport. Some couplings and linkages on roller coasters can be 8 to 15 times stronger than required. It is the responsibility of the manufacturers to produce a safe design and much investment goes into this aspect of new schemes.

The Tussauds Group employs an independent firm of inspection engineers that is involved from the earliest project meetings, right the way through to the handing over of the certificate that allows rides to be opened to the public. Much of the safety work involves standard procedures that don't need to involve a director of design on a day-to-day basis.

The paradox with roller coasters is that people are meant to get a thrill from the perceived danger of the ride but also feel totally comfortable in putting themselves on it.

> The one thing that is fun when it comes to riding a roller coaster is the uncertainty. You know it's safe but you are putting yourself in peril – is it going to leave the track? People want that adrenalin rush and to know, deep down, it's safe. People come to Alton Towers and they are given a clear impression that this is a serious business. Our industry's safety record is superb. It is far more hazardous travelling *to* a theme park than enjoying yourself *at* a theme park.
>
> If you suffer from motion sickness, you've got no worries with Air, because Air is physically not that demanding, it's a very lovely exhilarating feeling. Everybody that has expressed concern over riding Air has always said afterwards that it was a lovely experience. Nemesis is the intense one.

2.5.1 Maintenance of rides

One of the Tussauds Group's criteria for short-listing potential manufacturers concerns the information provided about the amount of person hours required to inspect and maintain a ride. Once the manufacturer signs off a ride the maintenance schedule is the responsibility of the maintenance department at Alton Towers.

Each component of a roller coaster is replaceable, and if a ride is well maintained, it can last almost indefinitely. Few rides by John Wardley have been pensioned off and most are still operating as they were intended. The real problem faced by roller coasters is a loss of popularity brought about by newer and more exciting rides in the theme parks and amusement parks but even this process can take decades for an effect to become noticeable. Unfortunately the number of years a ride remains popular cannot easily be written into the brief.

The customers at Alton Towers probably think less about downtime than they do about safety but downtime is a vital aspect of successful roller coaster design. Manufacturers have to guarantee the availability of the ride for a specified number of days when the park is open and there are penalties for the manufacturer if the ride is out of commission for more than the agreed time. It doesn't have to operate all year of course. At Alton Towers there is a long close season during the winter months when all the significant maintenance can be carried out.

A ride like Air or Nemesis should be out of use for no more than a fraction of 1 per cent of its working time. If a ride is down for five minutes a day this will almost certainly have a huge repercussion. If a ride stops, it might have to be evacuated. Also there might be 1000 or 1500 people in the system queuing for it. The fact the ride has gone down for five minutes in ten hours on a particular day can influence the perceptions of 10 per cent of the customers in the park that day.

Where possible, day-to-day and weekly maintenance is carried out at night because people expect all the rides to be available. Many of the rides are highly sophisticated pieces of engineering. Air, for example, undergoes a series of maintenance checks on its mechanical and computer control systems every night. Checks completed, the trains glide empty to their morning start positions.

The maintenance is needed both for safety and to keep customers happy. Unlike pay-per-ride parks, Alton Towers charges for admission (pay-one-price) after which there is no further payment for rides. If a ride is out of service in a pay-per-ride park, there might be customer disappointment but it's not compounded by a feeling of having paid for something that has not been received. Alton Towers is very keen that customers leave the park with a very positive feeling about their experience and this means maximising the availability of rides and other resources.

During each close season, the track of each ride will be tested. Critical sections of track – those subjected to high-speed traffic or high forces are X-rayed and magnetic-particle tested. These are two types of non-destructive test used to look for defects such as cracks hidden inside components or welds. All the trains are stripped down and the condition and performance of critical components is checked.

2.5.2 Funding new developments

Few manufacturers possess the capability to make every component and every assembly in any given product, and roller coaster manufacturers are no different. In the case of B&M only the design is undertaken at the base in Switzerland. All other manufacturing is subcontracted out. It has track fabrication plants in Switzerland, America and Spain. All its vehicles are assembled in Switzerland.

Some amusement parks market themselves on the qualities of particular rides and offer very little in terms of the local park environment. Other parks seek to offer a total quality experience – for example, the experience when moving between rides or using other facilities. Clearly, these different strategies have implications for the way each park funds new development.

For parks that focus on the rides the most significant cost in developing a new ride is the ride hardware – the track, the trains, and so on. This can account for up to 80 per cent of the budget with 10 per cent being spent on the civil engineering such as the laying of foundations and the remaining 10 per cent on erecting the structure, the buildings and the queuing systems. Like other major capital projects there will frequently be an initial phase where seed funding enables the company to assess the feasibility of a proposal before committing itself to the full investment.

At Alton Towers the proportion of the budget allocated to the ride hardware is usually limited to around 50 per cent because of the importance of the ground works to the presentation of each ride. Ground work includes landscaping and general decoration of the ride but it also includes vital aspects that are often frequently underestimated by the public such as the way a ride has been styled, its name and the way it has been marketed. The branding of a ride can be a huge revenue earner for a group like Tussauds.

> Air, for example, was a gigantic branding exercise. We came up with an innovative roller coaster but there was a lot of scepticism about the idea of calling it Air and presenting it in a sky blue livery. However, it's turned out to be a hugely successful brand with all sorts of merchandising and marketing spin-offs [Figure 28].

Figure 28 Air ride branding attaches excitement to spin-offs

With rides costing many millions of pounds (Colossus at Thorpe Park in Surrey cost an estimated £10 million and Air is estimated to have cost £12 million) the design and installation of a new ride is a major decision for any park. Recouping that investment is subject to a number of factors. The finances of a pay-one-price operation can be quite complicated because the ride itself doesn't earn any money; it makes a contribution to pulling people to the park. At a park like Blackpool Pleasure Beach where the public pay as they go on each ride it's much easier to compare the amount of money a ride has taken with its costs over a year.

2.5.3 Future innovations

In my conversation with John Wardley I returned to the subject of the proposed wooden roller coaster for Alton Towers and, more generally, to speculation on future innovations in the roller coaster industry. At the time of writing (summer 2003) the new woodie is still only at the planning stage and little information exists in the public domain. Given that Alton Towers has a worldwide reputation for innovative and highly sophisticated rides I was keen to explore John Wardley's approach to this more traditional style of attraction. I asked him if he had a clear vision of what the ride would be like and whether he thought it would be innovative in some way.

> I have a fairly clear vision of what we want. The whole premise of this is that we want to present to our guests a traditional-looking, large roller coaster. If, subsequently, a manufacturer came up with a minimalist steel design as we used in Air this wouldn't match my vision. What works for Air probably wouldn't work in a wooden coaster. That's not to say it should be the exact recreation of an old wooden coaster. There might be opportunities to create the experience of a woodie while exploiting the advantages of modern materials and processes. For example, I'm looking at ways we might prefabricate the track but in a way that recreates the look and apparently behaves like traditional coaster tracking albeit rather more precisely by using modern technology.

Throughput of customers appears to be a focus for development. There are likely to be innovations in queuing systems in all of the major parks as companies seek to improve the user experience. Theme parks have a reputation for queues and companies are very sensitive about the effect this can have on customers visiting and those planning to visit. There are rarely problems at off-peak times but at busy periods like bank holidays the wait for rides can be long. Companies like the Tussauds Group are constantly working on improvements to throughput in the various parks.

Carrying capacity is another important indicator. Alton Towers would have great difficulty justifying any major new ride that didn't accommodate – and achieve – at least 1000 people per hour. On a good day Alton Towers receives around 18 000 visitors and most of these want to ride the rides. Ideally all the rides would record figures of about 1500 people an hour but that's not always possible. Some rides at Alton Towers have a very high capacity and one ride can achieve 1800 to 2000 people an hour. A ride with a single loading station is always going to be more difficult to get up to these very high throughput figures. The CAD software has a role here too.

In this programme I can specify load and unload times – which might typically be between 30 seconds, and 1 minute 15 seconds – and adapt this to suit particular disability groups. Once loaded, it is safe for the train to leave the station and it will start to climb this lift but until this second train has gone safely through these brakes the programme won't let it go over the top of the lift. If there was an emergency and one train was stopped by a set of brakes the other train would be slowed or stopped well before its ascent.

The programme can be made to simulate various conditions. Normally the two trains will pass approximately in the middle of this particular course but if the despatch of one train was delayed because of slow unloading or loading or if the temperature of the track varied or if one train had considerably more passengers than the other, they could be allowed to pass at a different point, that is, without intervention. The simulation can be left to run for a little while and it provides figures for the average carrying capacity achieved under these conditions.

2.6 Satisfactions and future developments

I asked John about what gave him satisfaction in his career as a roller coaster designer.

The thing that pleases me about Air, Oblivion and Nemesis is that … although they are gigantic pieces of machinery, our guests, the end users, regard them as 'personalities'. They regard them as monsters, creatures or things that are intimidating. … Of course that is what entertainment is all about. … They think of Nemesis as some kind of organic creature. Oblivion on the other hand is 'techno'; they think of that as some kind of high-tech personality. Air is much more ethereal – it's floating and flying.

Nemesis was a great challenge. We had to create our own quarry … shifting thousands of tonnes of rock in order to bury that machine in the ground. It was burying it in the ground that gave Nemesis its unique personality. Oblivion was also buried in the ground; we tunnelled and created a mine shaft deep underground. Air we lifted up. We couldn't go above treetops therefore it was quite a challenge to be able to get height into the ride within the constraints of the site. But Air is more about lightness. Air is the 'hero' whereas Nemesis and Oblivion are the 'villains'.

Although each ride has it's own distinct personality, strip all that away and you're left with exactly the same things – concrete, steel, bearings chains, motors and fibreglass.

Finally, I asked John about his thoughts on future theme park rides.

The ride everyone talks about is the Spiderman ride at Universal Studios in Islands of Adventure in Florida. It is basically a combination of ride, simulator and 3D film and it's fantastic, absolutely amazing. It cost an absolute fortune but money hasn't simply been thrown at it, it's very clever indeed. It is the most amazing ride experience in the world. It has a motion base that goes along the track through real sets but you are also wearing 3D glasses. There are large projection screens built into the sets and you cannot tell what is real and what is illusion because the motion base is spinning you around, accelerating you and pointing you in different directions. I don't think we'll see one in the UK in the near future – it has almost crippled Islands of Adventure financially.

3 Case study 3 Trannon furniture – sustainability in action

3.1 Introduction

It is possible you will have seen, or even used, some of the furniture designed and produced by Trannon Ltd. Although it has a modest factory and showroom in the depths of the Wiltshire countryside the furniture is represented in some of the most prestigious new building and architectural renovation schemes in the UK. The company occupies a 4000 square metre building near Salisbury in Wiltshire and this houses the various storerooms and workshops and a showroom (Figure 29).

Figure 29 Trannon workshops and showroom in Wiltshire, England

Trannon's corporate customers include the Scottish Parliament (designed and made furniture for the reception), the National Trust, the Crafts Council, the Royal Fine Art Commission for Scotland, the Imperial War Museum, and the award-winning National Museum of Wales (Figure 30). Trannon's furniture has been on show at venues worldwide, including London's Design Museum, the Smithsonian in Washington DC, the Rhode Island School of Design, the New York International Contemporary Furniture Fair, Cologne Handwork museum and Collect at London's V&A museum.

Figure 30 Trannon furniture in the National Museum of Wales

(a) Cardiff bench

(b) Four-seat bench

Trannon does not merely produce beautiful and usable furniture. With over 20 years of impeccable ecological integrity its founder, David Colwell, is one of the pioneers of *sustainable design* and clean production in the UK. Trannon uses mostly green timber, which is air-dried to about 30 per cent moisture content. A newly felled tree contains about twice as much water as cellular material, expressed as 200 per cent moisture content. In contrast, the kiln-dried timber supplied by most timber merchants would have a moisture content of 8–12 per cent.

Various manufacturing techniques have been exploited and developed. Trannon is particularly well known for the use of steam bending. This not only creates elegant and appropriate curves but it also seasons the timber quickly, using a fraction of the energy of kiln drying. Trannon also uses woodland thinnings – the immature and usually unwanted trees that naturally occur in timber plantations – and these are obtained locally. Such thinnings offer many benefits to a designer who knows how to exploit their unique characteristics.

This study examines Trannon furniture. It presents the background to some of its most successful products. It also illustrates a broad interpretation of sustainability to include social, economic and environmental factors as well as the more focused ecodesign aspects of many products today. Trannon provides an opportunity to study a successful furniture business for which the notion of sustainability is central, embracing, for example, the prosperity of the local community, rural employment and forest management. However, before I turn to the company I'll look a little more closely at the issues underpinning sustainability in the timber furniture industry today. The following quote comes from the Trannon website (**www.trannon.co.uk**).

Furniture for life

Trees are the world's only renewable structural material and timber is responsible for a third of Britain's trade deficit. 90 per cent of Britain's timber is imported and, every year, almost half our timber crop is pulped, burned or left to rot. The problem is that industry looks for tall, branchless trees and the isolated oak is neither.

To grow usable trees, the forester has to plant trees close together, discouraging them from branching. In the competition for light, each tree also reaches higher, trying to out-grow other trees. Before the forest matures, four out of five trees will have to be felled or thinned.

Ash thinnings are ideal for chair making because, being fast grown, they are able to absorb more shock than almost all mature trees. Vigorously growing young trees also fix more carbon from the atmosphere than a mature forest. In Britain, thinnings are ignored as a by-product of forestry. An enormous amount is sold cheaply for pulp or firewood. The more marginal sizes are simply left to rot.

Trannon has been pioneering new ways of using unseasoned thinnings sourced from local woodlands to minimise transport, and specialising in steam bending, which curves and seasons the timber simultaneously.

Not only are these bends stronger than the common laminations, this thinking also eliminates the need for kiln drying and provides early forestry income for management into the future. For this thinking, they received the FX Green Seating award in 1994.

(Trannon advertisement, 2003)

3.2 Company background and mission

Trannon was established by David Colwell in the 1970s and he still directs the company today in collaboration with his business partner Roy Tam. It's not incidental that both of them are designers. David Colwell (Figure 31) trained in furniture design at the Royal College of Art (RCA) in London. He then ran his own design practice. Roy Tam (Figure 32) also studied at the RCA but he followed the industrial design pathway, largely because his first degree had been medical electronics at Salford University. Subsequently at Cambridge Consultants Roy Tam worked with clients such as loudspeaker maker Celestion, Black & Decker USA, Gent, Guinness and NASA. He has been a member of the Design Council selection panel and received the BraunPrize for industrial design.

Figure 31 David Colwell holding a version of the C3 chair

Figure 32 Roy Tam in the Trannon showroom

3.2.1 Early developments in sustainability

The early 1990s saw some major developments to the company but the roots of its mission are to be found in the 1970s and 1980s when David Colwell perceived significant divisions between manufacturing industry and the social and cultural climate in which it operated. At this time most furniture buyers, and indeed most furniture makers, failed to appreciate the resources they worked with or the implications of their use.

Take wood for example. For most manufacturers it arrived kiln-dried and cut into particular sections, sizes and lengths. Increasingly, designers were working with a material that was becoming divorced from its original qualities and its original source. Few manufacturers were aware of the wider cultural, social and environmental implications of purchasing and using timber.

One dramatic and widely reported consequence has been the deforestation of tropical regions due to an unnecessary demand for exotic hardwoods. David Colwell realised the implications of such blinkered attitudes and determined to demonstrate that it was possible to combine successful business with a sensitivity to materials selection and sustainability.

Thirty years ago, David Colwell was one among a very small number of people who foresaw the importance of sustainability to British industry – and particularly with reference to wood. Timber offers numerous opportunities for environmentally sensitive production, not least because it is a resource that grows. Even the waste, the so-called by-products of modern forestry practice and manufacturing in timber, can be used. (The following quotations are by Roy Tam unless otherwise stated).

> Take for example a plantation of ash trees [Figure 33]. A forester would plant five trees in high density to make them grow straight but over time he or she would thin (cut away) four to leave one mature tree. These thinnings can be very useful for making furniture. In many ways they are vastly better than mature trees. Also they can be harvested locally, using smaller lorries, which means less environmental pollution arising from transportation. We make considerable use of steam bending in our production processes. Steaming simultaneously seasons and softens the timber components allowing them to be put into jigs and bent into graceful curves. When cool and dry these curved components are immensely strong. It can be a very energy efficient process, overcoming the need for three weeks of kiln drying – especially when you consider that, in the furniture industry as a whole, up to 40 per cent of such kiln-dried timber is lost as offcuts.

Figure 33 Managed ash woodland

> But using thinnings and steam bending is only part of the story. If we are to have a truly sustainable process there has to be benefits to the land, the local economy and the wider social and natural environment. If you own a piece of land from which trees will only give you an income after 100 years you're not going to benefit. So by using thinnings we enable foresters to generate income early in the life of a plantation. Up until now thinnings have only really been used to make things like squash racquets, spade handles, hammer handles and broom heads but all those industries have now been replaced by plastics or cheap imports, which means it is cheaper to buy the whole hammer than to make the handle.

Figure 34 High stool

> Thinnings have two other significant advantages over mature trees arising from their fast rate of growth. Firstly young wood is very ductile and is resistant to splitting. In an old tree you can see the growth rings are very close together. Older wood is more brittle but less dense. In thinnings the growth rings are spaced more widely apart. Secondly the fast rate of growth means young trees are absorbing more carbon from the atmosphere. In fact a fast-growing tree can absorb 20–30 times more CO_2 in one year than a slow growing tree. I think that's quite a lot of benefits.

Today all Trannon's chairs are still made from thinnings although different parts of a tree will go into different products to make the most of its natural characteristics (the High stool in Figure 34 incorporates thinnings). Sales from a range of sixteen furniture products account for about half the turnover, with corporate commissions making up the other half of the business. The range currently includes six chairs, six tables and an assortment of shelving, sofas, and sideboards.

3.2.2 Aims of Trannon's designs

In addition to the aims concerning sustainability Trannon aims to produce furniture that is as comfortable, attractive and as usable as possible. Ergonomics is only half the story. Block 1 closely examined the act of sitting and you saw how chairs could only partly address the needs of a dynamic human body. Chairs can constrain, they can hold the sitter still when there is a need to move, and Trannon has confronted this problem by devising chairs that assist the sitter to remain active, for example by offering a rocking motion. You might remember that the Balans chair shown in Block 1 Section 2 similarly encourages users to adopt active sitting. But designing a chair that encourages users to adopt an appropriate posture doesn't necessarily mean it will be commercially successful as Roy Tam explains:

> We have one particular chair, the Act One [Figure 35] in which the user can balance or gently rock. It is perfect for active sitting and we envisioned it as an ideal home-office computer chair. However, we cannot market it for office use because a VDU operator's chair has to be adjustable in all directions. We designed a chair that requires no adjustment but because of this it doesn't fully meet the necessary regulations. It's a great chair but we cannot market it as an office chair.

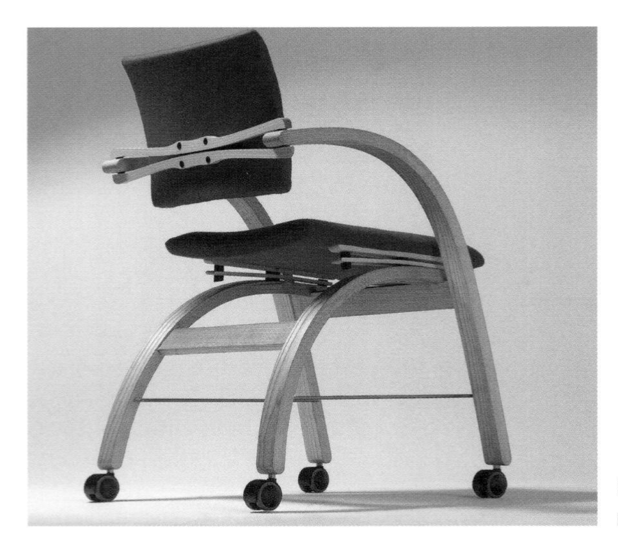

Figure 35 Act One reactive castor chair

Using Trannon products is intended to be a pleasurable experience. No matter how successful a manufacturer is from the sustainability point of view if the products are not functional and attractive there will be no sales and hence no opportunity to practise sustainable manufacture.

When Trannon designs a table or dining chairs it considers the social interactions of the likely users. It wants people to savour the rituals of dining, to linger over the courses. This illustrates the important psychological and sociological aspects of usability.

One of the most important applications for social-design thinking is in the furniture for public spaces. If you go to the National Museum of Wales you will see seating designed by Trannon 10 years ago that broke many of the conventional rules for such large open interior public spaces. The company worked with the architect to contrive seating in the centre of the galleries.

Trannon devised a unique system of bench seating that allows sitters to spin around to look at the displays – a dramatic contrast to the types of bench seats seen in airports and other waiting areas. From a social point of view sitters cannot only view the works of art but they can turn to a friend for conversation or share a snack. And children love them – an important factor for schools and families visiting the gallery. In the making of the Four-seat bench (Figure 30), 200 cm diameter green (undried) ash is turned and sawn along its axis to relieve drying stresses. It is then steam bent using a former and straps (discussed later, in subsection 3.6).

3.3 Design process at Trannon

As this course closely examines the design process one of my questions to Roy Tam concerned Trannon's strategy for generating creative new ideas and converting them into marketable products. I'll look at generating ideas first.

> We get ideas in three different ways. Firstly we might simply have a hunch – we sit in chairs, we use tables, we discuss existing products and we see opportunities to set higher standards than current products. It's like testing a car. You sit in it and you find some things aren't right. It's a process that is rarely formalised as design activity, it can happen anytime, anywhere. If you're observant and you care about your environment you get hunches for improving things all the time. [This is the constructive discontent referred to in Blocks 2 and 3.] Secondly, we listen to other people. People comment on our work all the time. They tell us what they like and they ask why we don't do such-and-such and this will start us thinking. Thirdly, we get specific and detailed requests to build furniture. This is the least enjoyable way of being creative.

A great deal of experimentation goes on in the workshops and, clearly, working directly with timber is an aid to creativity. Some projects begin with a very rough sketch in pencil or pen (see Figure 36) but many more originate in experiments with particular materials, techniques or processes.

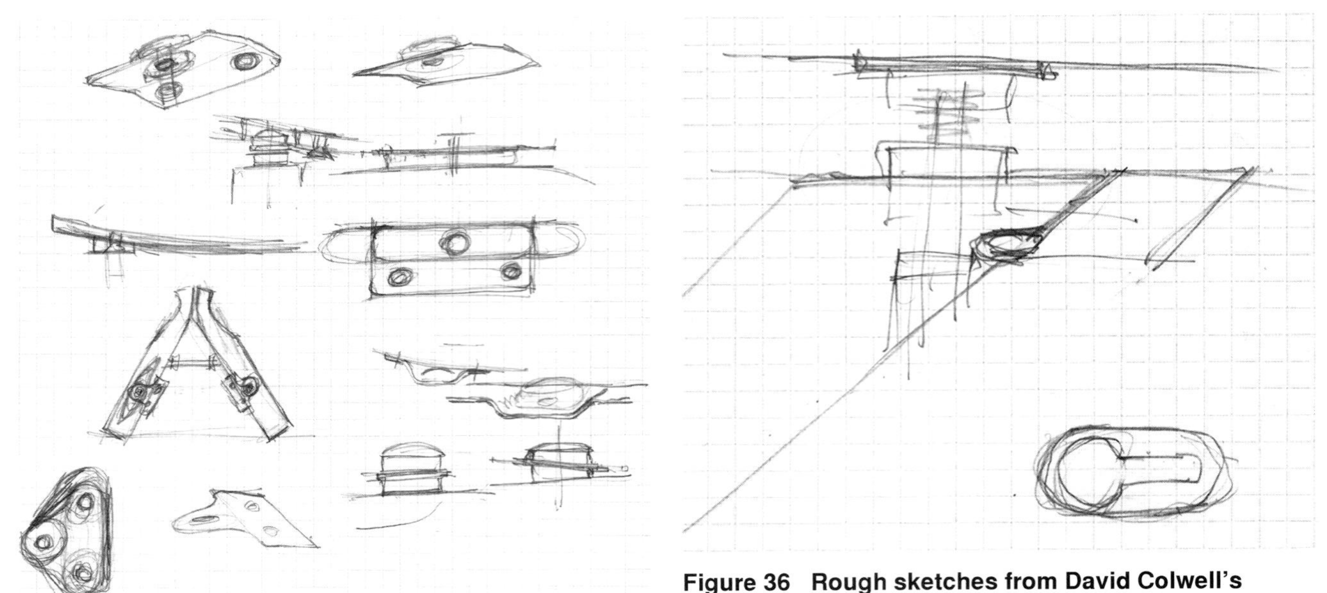

Figure 36 Rough sketches from David Colwell's notebook

3.3.1 Trannon's prototypes

Prototyping is an essential activity for Trannon. Many of its commissions require small innovations or developments to existing products to suit a particular client. In the development of the Springback chair (see Figure 39 in subsection 3.5), for example, it had to produce several prototypes of the joint between the stainless steel bracings and the steam-bent ash frame. A two-part epoxy resin is used to bond the steel to the wood. As the wood at this point had a very thin wall thickness the resin could sometimes squeeze through the wood grain and on to the surface and Trannon had to produce a number of prototypes in order to overcome this. In all cases they require a joint to be stronger than the wood around it so if the junctions of the steel and wood in the Springback chair appear rather delicate to you, remember the epoxy resin has bonded the components so they act as a single strong unit.

At the moment Trannon sees no need to use computer-aided design techniques at the conceptual end of designing. The company views the construction of full-size, rough models and prototypes as more valuable. These allow a visual evaluation, a sit-on test, and an examination of joint details. Roy Tam believes it avoids the tunnel vision that CAD can encourage. The relatively small size of the batches produced and the incorporation of craft techniques mean that CAD is likely to be less relevant than it might be to a mass-market furniture manufacturer that might also seek to exploit computer-aided manufacture – for example, numerically controlled machines for drilling, routing and shaping.

For Trannon, a full-size prototype allows the material and the shapes to provide essential feedback to the design team. Skilled eyes can detect where one wood might be preferable over another, where shaping a part differently may relieve potential stresses, or which process might best suit a particular component. In fact, such full-size models and prototypes can be a major determinant of whether a concept gets the go ahead to go into production. Modelling and prototyping can give rise to creative new ideas. For example, Trannon hopes to explore the use of thin strips of waste wood – weaving them like a basket into furniture forms or combining wood with fleece in new ideas for seating.

3.3.2 Concept design

As with many small companies a great deal of time is taken up with management and administration so time for creative exploration of ideas is limited. Currently about 10 per cent of time is devoted to concept design – usually by slotting activities in between production jobs.

> When I have an idea, I try to improve it by asking David to deliberately misinterpret the concept I describe to him verbally. I'll often restrain from drawing it so that my descriptions can be more ambiguous, but I might ask him to draw back to me what he thought I meant. That way I might get many ideas from the original thought.

An order from a museum provides a good illustration of the creative dialogue at Trannon. In 1997 a museum ordered 30 stacking chairs from the company. One of the client's primary requirements was that these chairs should link together, which meant that Trannon had to devise some modifications for this particular batch. Over a meal one evening David Colwell and Roy Tam began by exploring ideas for a linking mechanism but soon realised children would make up a significant part of the user group for these chairs, for example in school outings. There was no denying it, the museum had ordered the wrong chair – it needed to be more fun.

So Colwell and Tam contacted the museum to outline a proposal for a very different type of seat. As the chairs would always be used linked together it was proposed that each chair only had two legs. The chair units and the linking mechanism would meet the client's brief by complying with fire regulations, using various curved and S-shaped arrangements of varying lengths and being easy to store. The Link bench was born (Figure 37). It was also cost effective to make, partly due to the low number of components.

Figure 37 Link bench

I asked Roy Tam about what Block 2 referred to as the 'design before the design' – including the use of a brief and a specification in typical work at Trannon.

> When we embark on a commission we prefer to write the brief. It's far more productive if we meet with the client and compose a brief rather than have to question things in their brief. In our own designs we can be as loose as we like. In the case of a sofa design we just said we want a sofa for ourselves, to have a siesta in it and we don't want it to be heavily stuffed with foam and upholstery.

Establishing a selling price can also vary from a tightly specified to an unspecified figure. With the Act One chair (Figure 35) for example, Trannon simply set out to produce the best that the material and the technology would allow. Although much larger furniture companies with generous design budgets and comprehensive tooling capabilities can produce chairs at a low unit price, Trannon has the advantage of flexibility.

The nature of Trannon's production process means tooling costs can be low and capital tied up in raw materials need only be modest. This means Trannon is more flexible and can change direction or respond to new ideas more quickly than larger competitors. If you consider a car or some other mass manufactured consumer item that requires huge investments in tooling, it's often impossible to make changes late in the development process because of the costs that have been committed. Trannon is pleased that it still has the flexibility to make improvements to a product even during the production process. All of Trannon's designs are continually evolving.

3.4 Design for users

One of the central themes of this course has been the involvement of users in the design process and I was keen to explore how Trannon managed to integrate users into the design and development of its products.

> David tends to seek people's feedback on designs via, for example, dinner parties with friends. I often run ideas past my wife who is a physiotherapist and in one current project we hope to work with a consultant osteopath to develop a chair and conduct formal tests. We also worked with Design Age at the Helen Hamlyn Research Centre (at the Royal College of Art) to learn about older people's needs. [Examples of other design work from the Helen Hamlyn Research Centre are on the course DVD.]

Common wisdom suggests a little bit of knowledge can be a dangerous thing and the subject of ergonomics is no exception.

> Take seat height for example. There are many examples of work seats on the market and designers have slowly discovered that simply making a seat adjustable can be totally ineffective. If you are short you will raise the seat and as a result your feet will be off the ground or at least you'll be in an uncomfortable posture. The proper procedure is to start with your feet on the floor, adjust the height of the chair and then adjust the height of the table to go with the chair. However, there are not enough tables that are height adjustable. If we extend this thinking to dining tables it creates new problems. Traditionally a dining table has been one consistent height but this doesn't have to be the case. A height adjustable worktable for home use is one area of interest for us.

3.5 From concept to production

After the concept phase of design, what is done to convert creative concepts into successful products? For Trannon the process is guided by the need to ensure a quality product emerges at the end. The resulting furniture must not only look good, it must possess an integrity – an honesty in materials, processes and engineering. It's this integrity that links Trannon's products together across a diverse range and that lies at the heart of the company's success.

3.5.1 Importance of engineering

It may seem strange to talk of engineering in this wood-dominated manufacturing company that apparently relies so much on good, old-fashioned craftsmanship. However, if the various activities that lead to an excellent example of furniture design are disentangled, there are parallels with engineering processes found in other industries. Engineering chairs can be extremely difficult and the skills and knowledge required can be different to those required, say, in engineering a table. Usually chairs need to be light but Trannon also believes chairs should be flexible to allow the practice of active sitting discussed earlier. It believes flexible chairs can add to comfort, strength and an extended life for the furniture.

Tables on the other hand need to be stable structures. Usually they need to be stiff but in the case of a four-leg table you might want it to twist slightly in order to accommodate uneven floors. Of course the designer might exploit a three-legged table to overcome this problem. In fact Trannon exploits both the twisting, four-leg principle and the three-leg principle in its table designs. The GTX glass dining table (Figure 38) is a good example of the former where the flexibility of the crossframe allows the X-frame ends a certain degree of independence so that the table can accommodate uneven floors.

Figure 38 GTX glass dining table

> We will never miss an opportunity to use three legs if we can. Traditionally a four-leg chair that is also very stiff will rock when the sitter is using it on an uneven surface. This rocking will place considerable forces onto the joints, which often break or become loose. Our attitude is to design these chairs so as to allow key joints to move

because that will make the chair last longer. However, I think people don't always appreciate this advantage. A potential buyer might assume a flexible chair will have a shorter lifespan but this is not the case. We have even called one of our recent products the Springback chair to emphasise the comfort arising from its dynamic structure.

Figure 39 C10 Springback chair. Steam bent ash frame with stainless-steel bracing, and seat in pressed ash or upholstered.

Figure 40 C3 Stacking chair

Figure 41 C3 Stacking chair used as café seating

Figure 42 C6 Captain's chair. Steam bent and turned ash.

3.5.2 Design features in Trannon's tables and chairs

Trannon has evolved two design features that offer high levels of comfort in its chairs. The first of these is the use of a split central spine in the backrest. This can be seen in the Springback chair (Figure 39) and the C3 Stacking chair (Figures 40 and 41). The gap in the backrests means the human backbone doesn't contact the wood, which overcomes the need for upholstery in this area.

The second feature is the use of a wraparound component that enfolds the sitter as if they were sitting in a rubber ring or ring doughnut. The C3 and C6 chairs (Figures 40 and 42) display this feature. Given that these chairs are purchased because they can be used for different functions the wraparound backrest provides comfort when users sit upright (for example when dining), lean forward (for example office work) or swivel sideways (for example in conversation). The fact the C3 will stack is also a significant advantage as this clears spaces for other uses when the chairs are not required. The C3s look good even when they are stacked.

I considered adjustability in tables earlier and it's clear that in selecting a table to sit at there are two important features to consider – the height of the surface and the clearance for sitters' knees. As all solid timber tables will usually have a frame as well as a top surface there can be quite a difference between the height of the surface and the clearance for a sitter's knees. Traditionally a table maker could either define the ideal surface height and then try to make a frame that allowed sufficient knee clearance or they could start with the knee clearance – perhaps using a typical seat as a starting point – and allow the overall table height to emerge.

Some tables today incorporate a low cross rail, which merely provides another obstacle to comfortable sitting. Trannon has attempted to overcome this problem in its dining table where the top acts as a significant structural member and not just as a surface. Strength is introduced via cleverly curved end sections that ensure stability in the tabletops. In many cases Trannon tables have no rails or structures beneath the table surface. As Trannon only designs in solid timber, most of the jointing techniques in the tables are designed to accommodate movement arising from the natural movements of solid timber, which is typically 5 per cent across the grain.

3.5.3 Role of drawing

This course has also looked at the role of drawing in the product development process and I asked Roy Tam about his views on the value of drawing.

> It is critical to produce drawings for jobs. It's like writing a specification, if you don't have a guide such as a drawing or a specification then whatever can go wrong will go wrong. We use drawings in different ways. We particularly enjoy making full-size drawings in the process of designing new pieces of furniture. Chairs are lovely things to draw full-size because you get a feel for appropriateness of size or details of a joint. Such full-size drawings are essential in production. As well as the images, full-size drawings usually present various written notes to guide the operator in converting the 2D image into a 3D item. In theory, someone on the shop floor should be able to make the item with nothing other than the full-size drawing. In practice, we personally point out clever procedures in detail, which is critical to us working smart. At other times I might use a 2D drafting package on the computer to modify stock components. Data on all our standard designs are available from our computers.

So there is some evidence of computer-aided design at Trannon but computers also have a valuable role in presentation. Digital photographs of scale models are increasingly used in presentations to clients or when discussing potential commissions. They can be particularly effective for discussions via e-mail. It can enable Colwell or Tam to illustrate new concepts beyond their current product range.

3.6 Steam bending

The basic principle of steam bending is that timber components are placed inside a container, in temperatures around 100°C, which is continuously charged with steam. One or two hours in this atmosphere is sufficient to soften the wood, and when it is removed from the steam it has to be bent around a former or jig within 20 seconds – a shorter cycle time than a similar sized injection moulding. When cool and dry the wood retains the curved shape but, like many plastic materials, wood has a memory and if it was put back into the steamer it would return to its original shape.

Of course wooden parts could be cut into curved shapes but the advantage of steam bending is that the fibres of the wood are made to follow the intended curve, resulting in parts with great strength and some flexibility. Steam bending is ideal for chair parts that experience large forces.

3.6.1 Techniques in steam bending

There are a number of techniques that ensure a smooth bending process. Firstly the outer face of the part being bent needs to be supported by a thin steel or nylon band. This is because the fibres are usually being stretched. If they were unsupported as they were bent around the former they could easily fracture. Trannon has devised a jig whereby the strap and the wood are held tightly together so that no stretching takes place on the outer surface. The support redirects the bending forces inwards where the wood fibres are compressed.

Figure 43 shows the stages of steam bending a length of wood that has a section of approximately 50 mm × 20 mm.

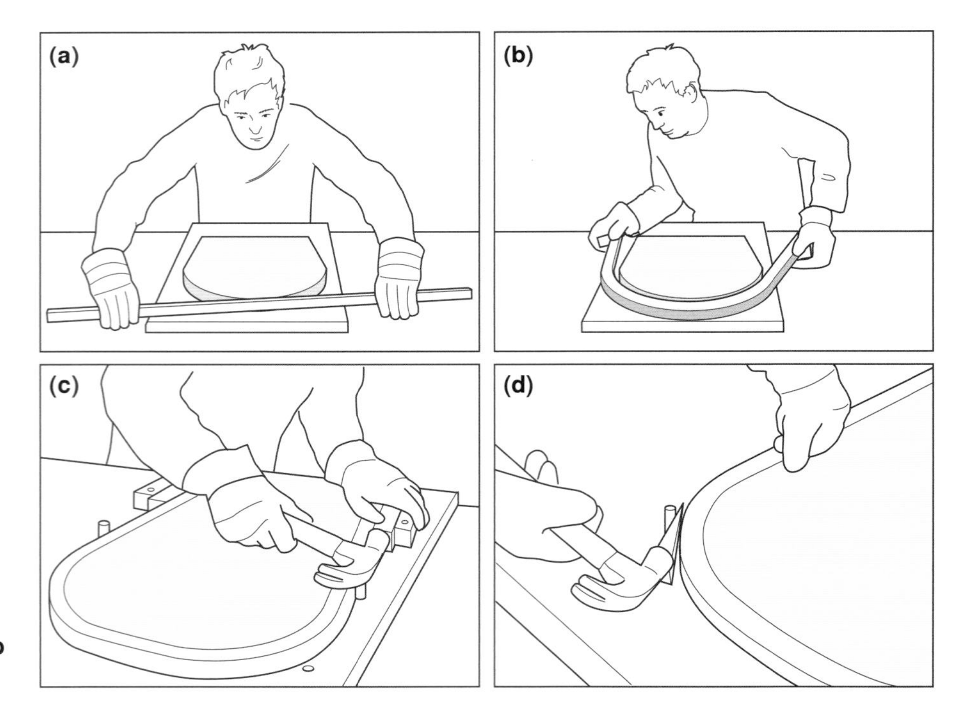

Figure 43 Stages in steam bending

(a) Position the steamed strip

(b) With strip cramped, use a strap to pull both sides round the former

(c) Secure sides with wedges and put dowels into holes in base

(d) Release strap and push strip toward former by using wedges

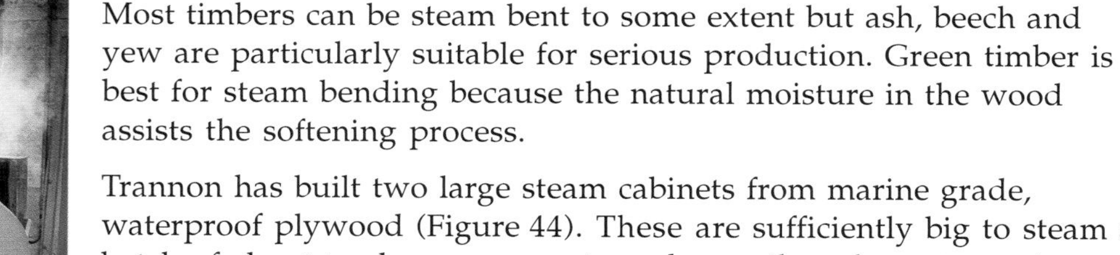

Figure 44 Removing wooden components from a steam oven at Trannon

Most timbers can be steam bent to some extent but ash, beech and yew are particularly suitable for serious production. Green timber is best for steam bending because the natural moisture in the wood assists the softening process.

Trannon has built two large steam cabinets from marine grade, waterproof plywood (Figure 44). These are sufficiently big to steam a batch of about twelve components such as rails or legs at one time. However, it's relatively easy for the DIY enthusiast to build a small steamer cabinet for the home workshop based on a steam wallpaper stripper. Trannon is currently exploring the use of its waste wood to power the steam cabinets.

The jigs vary in complexity depending on the shapes required and the frequency of use but even the most sophisticated are easily produced from plywood and timber found around the average workshop. They allow various clamps and wedges to be inserted to hold the bent wood to the formers for shaping. Often, the shaped pieces are transferred to drying jigs to free-up the shaping jigs, therefore enabling more pieces to be shaped in one batch. For the largest of Trannon's components, they are bent around the jig with the use of a hydraulic press. Most steam bent chair components can be removed from their jigs in ten minutes, put into drying jigs, and be usable within twelve hours.

Figure 45 Jigs used in the steam bending of backs to the Director's chair

One of the more unusual jigs is shown in Figure 45. This allows two compound-curve backs for the C2 Director's chair (Figure 46) to be bent in each jig – the forces in one balancing the forces in the other.

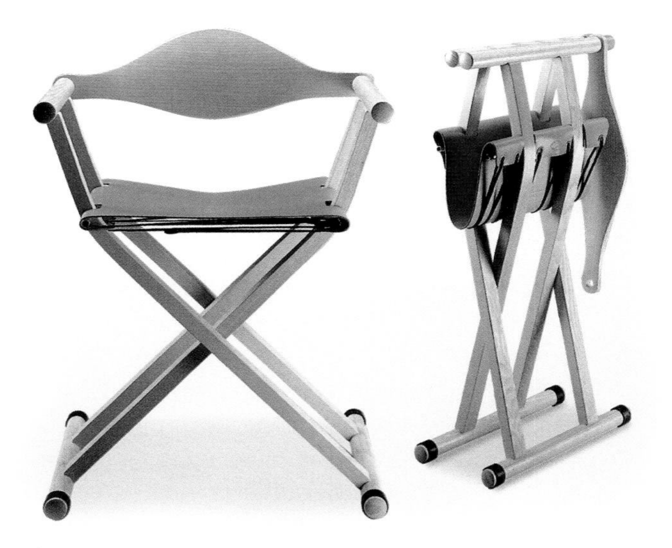

Figure 46 C2 Director's chair

3.6.2 Contrast between steam bending and lamination

Steam bending doesn't stop wood from shrinking and warping but the inaccuracies are more difficult to spot than they are in planed, flat sections. Of course the components will need final finishing because the steaming can slightly raise the fibres of the wood. What follows is my summary of the steam bending process compared with the lamination process discussed in Block 1.

Energy use

Steam bending is a low-energy process. The timber is not dried and the steam is easily generated. Lamination is a high-energy process. The timber must be kiln dried and cut into thin layers before lamination. There is also energy used in cutting off the waste material on the sides of each laminated component.

Chemical use

Lamination demands very strong adhesives to be used whereas steam bending requires no added chemicals in its production. Trannon also uses no harmful adhesives in construction. This has implications for staff working conditions and disposal of waste material.

Component tolerance

Lamination offers the ability to make parts with high accuracy and repeatability. Furniture designers using steam bending need to allow for small differences between components.

Strength and weight

Steaming offers lighter and less brittle components when compared to similar components produced by lamination.

3.7 Organisational issues

Trannon employs nine people with the majority of these based at the Wiltshire factory. One of the main reasons for this location is the accessibility to excellent sustainable timber supplies in the south of England. Additionally David Colwell has a design studio at his home in Powys, Wales and this provides a location for staff to gather to conduct design work away from the distractions of the workshops and showroom.

Given that Trannon is a relatively small company, effective communication within the organisation is relatively easy to achieve. Makers meet around a table at least once each week to discuss schedules and any problems with production. One of the key features of the organisation is the close working relationships that are possible between the design staff and those involved in production. The two-way dialogue enables production staff to suggest changes to components or processes and it enables the design staff to observe activities and to spot opportunities for making improvements. The making of prototypes involves both groups in a collaborative process aimed at efficiency in process and perfection in the product.

The British furniture industry comprises various types of business. There is a big difference between those that see themselves as craftsman-makers, which exist to create one-off commissions or low-volume production runs, and those companies that set out to supply the wider demand for furniture and produce their output in large batches. The difference is one of intent and philosophy.

Trannon views itself as being in neither category. It employs craftspeople but uses machines and mechanised processes where relevant (Figure 47), and hand techniques where they are the most effective means of achieving a desired result. It is an integration of craft and industrial design. Each product proposal calls for creative thinking about the methods of manufacture; every decision in a design has a consequence in production time, a consequence in tolerance of components, a consequence in usability, and a consequence for the life of the product.

Figure 47 Trannon workshops

This relationship between craft and industrial design is a fascinating one and I asked Roy Tam if Trannon was deliberately modelled on any examples of outstanding furniture companies from earlier decades.

> I think the people we admire are the unknown furniture makers – the unsung developers of the Windsor chair, for example [see Block 1 Figure 4]. The heart of a good furniture company lies in the making, in getting your hands dirty. It's through this that real knowledge is developed, real innovations and improvements can come about. The Windsor chair is a particularly good illustration. Like the originators of the Windsor chair we try to reduce time-consuming and space-consuming manufacturing stages such as clamping components together. Ideally our products are easy to machine, easy to assemble, and easy to store.

3.8 Endnote

So what can you learn from companies such as Trannon? Scale of an organisation seems to be significant. Trannon employs only nine staff and in this respect it is closer to the model of furniture manufacturers seen in countries such as Japan and Italy – two of the most efficient furniture manufacturing countries in the world. Also the close working of research and development with production would seem to be important. At Trannon there is daily interaction between design and production staff.

Size also seems to be significant. David Colwell believes once a unit reaches around 20 staff a manufacturer should consider opening a new unit. Smaller, local units would have an opportunity to better use the resources of a particular area, thereby reducing, say, transportation costs and effects. Such units could also contribute to a local or regional economy.

Currently the very low international transport costs mean it is cost effective for a manufacturer to buy, for example, cherry wood in America, ship it to China to get it converted into furniture and then to ship this to Europe for sale in cut-price furniture outlets. It's not a sustainable strategy for the planet. It's Trannon's philosophy that design and manufacturing needs to look to local resources, local expertise and regional markets if it is to establish a system with a long-term future.

Trannon is proud of its achievements. Such work doesn't come about easily and David Colwell is critical of much of what passes for good design today. Much of Trannon's output is the result of sensitive teamworking.

Clearly furniture, like so many other aspects of international consumer culture, is influenced by fashion. Trends, styles and tastes in furniture come and go, but perhaps not as swiftly as those in clothing or music. The media has an influence on this and has a responsibility. Television, magazines and the Internet communicate and propagate style and fashion to the public and in doing so they can exploit a generally poor understanding of the real priorities. People can be inspired to buy novelty, image or associations with the exotic when the media could do so much more to popularise the notion of, for example, sustainability. Bad design is made to seem desirable and good design is omitted or rarely promoted.

I asked Roy Tam if he thought design had been hijacked by the styling industry.

> Here at Trannon our success is based on integrity. A designer needs to understand the fundamentals such as materials and structure. You've got to know what goes on inside. If it's a radio you've got to know what display you need, what you need to control. If it's a chair, you've got to understand the forces in the structure and what the material wants to do. My best advice is to look for things you want to make better. James Dyson did. You don't always have to be an expert to spot where improvements can be made or ideas transferred from one context to another.

For Trannon, design would seem to be an integration of many factors – technological, social, economic and environmental. The staff combine knowledge, creative skills and a desire to see real improvements to material culture. Few pieces of furniture made today stand the test of time but Trannon's products reveal integrity in thought and integrity in design.

For many companies design is little more than a service – there is no in-house manufacturing to convert ideas into tangible products. There is consequently no mechanism for feeding back information from making to design.

My final question to Roy Tam concerned his perceptions of the changes that he had witnessed in design over recent years and changes to his own design process as he became older and more experienced.

> David and I have been making furniture for many years. I have noticed how designing for the market has become so important compared with the technical side of the process. We are getting more sensitive at noticing what people are *not* saying – trying to read between the lines when we meet with clients, helping them to tell us their requirements. Where possible I like to see the project through to delivery to the customer. It brings it full circle if the same person who quoted for the job is there to see it installed. I like to know that my ideas really do work for the client. And it provides an opportunity for new commissions. Overall? Design is about adding value and that's what I like about my work.

The point about design adding value is central to the course and it underpins much that appeared in the earlier blocks, particularly Block 2.

Case study 4
Cannon Avent – polymer babycare products

4.1 Introduction

Cannon Avent is one of the UK's major manufacturers of polymer and rubber products for babies, parents and toddlers. It supplies products to some of the biggest high street retailers, such as Boots. In 2002 the company turnover was £76 million and it employs 1100 workers at three sites in London (one of them is shown in Figure 48) and Suffolk. My contact at the company was Dawn Jones, one of a small number of in-house product designers, and this study presents Avent's design process with reference to a range of successful products.

Figure 48 Avent's premises, north London

4.2 Company background

Cannon Rubber Ltd was founded in 1936 by David Atkin, the father of the current managing director. At this time the company, based in Tottenham, made latex rubber products such as wellington boots and hot water bottles using rubber imported from Malaysia but, significantly, the company gained a reputation for high-quality teats that were stretched over the tops of glass feeding bottles for babies. In the early 1970s a period of expansion under the control of the present managing director, Edward Atkin, coincided with the timing of his own young family and the field of babycare products was brought sharply into focus. The company engineers were set the task of designing a better bottle and a better teat for babies and therefore the seeds were sown for a company that was to go on to become a world leader in babycare products.

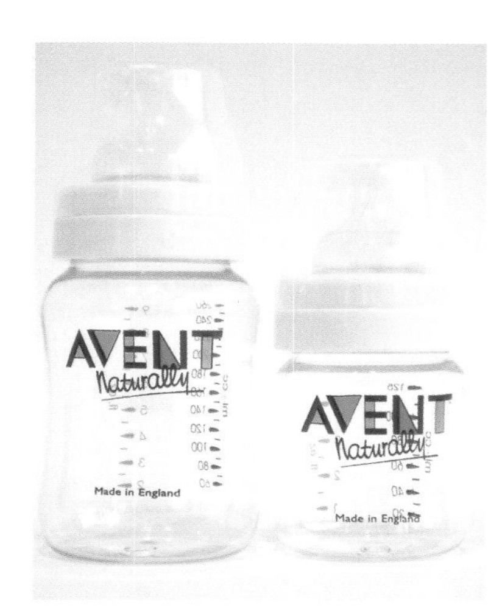

Figure 49 Avent wide-neck feeding bottles

In the 1960s the company began to exploit new polymer materials that offered acceptably high qualities of transparency and hygiene without the weight or danger of breakage that glass bottles presented. In 1982 Cannon devised and patented the first wide-neck feeding bottle that incorporated an integral valve in the teat. Originally named the Cannon Baby Safe, the feeding bottle significantly reduced occurrences of colic in babies and was a best seller. The Cannon brand can largely be traced back to this single product and its success gave a boost to many of the company's more utilitarian or unremarkable products at that time.

New ranges of plastic feeding bottles emerged (Figure 49) but it wasn't until 1984, when the company launched the brand 'Avent Naturally', that design was consistently applied to the product range leading to innovative and more usable products. Today the company can call upon decades of research, design and development experience in the field of polymer and particularly silicon rubber products.

Figure 50 Avent products on the shelves of a major retailer

The brand is now a world leader in babycare products and today the company supply products directly to major retailers (see Figure 50) and distributors such as Toys R Us, Babies R Us, Mothercare, and Boots. In recent years it has made major inroads to markets in the United States and now sells to Russia, China, all the European countries, and Scandinavia. Much of its success is attributable to the use of design across the organisation.

The products marketed by Avent today focus on the act of baby and child feeding but clearly this shades into several related activities. Due to its history in baby feeding products, the Avent brand has become associated with the age range from birth to six or twelve months but its product range includes items used well after this such as sterilisers, bottle warmers and the award winning Isis breast pump, as well as products for weaning and the toddler market. In doing this the company is moving away from its roots in rubber-based products but, if you reflect back to Block 2, it appears that the company knows what business it is really in. Today over 90 per cent of Avent's products are designed and made in-house. The company has received two Queen's Awards for Enterprise including one for innovation.

4.3 Company organisation

The company HQ in New Southgate, north London houses the concept design facilities along with other central activities such as accounts, some of the overseas sales and the IT department. Anything more than concept design usually requires collaboration with the technical staff based in Suffolk. The manufacturing plant at Glenford in Suffolk employs 650 people and allows the company to keep all the primary detail designing, manufacturing, assembly and some toolmaking in-house. The engineering department housed there is responsible for much of the final detail design of products. Additionally, Avent has a large factory producing rubber goods – mostly for the car industry – in Tottenham, quite close to the headquarters in New Southgate.

I was particularly keen to explore the relationship between concept design and engineering in the development of new and improved products.

The design department consists of three people – an industrial designer, a design engineer (my primary contact, Dawn Jones) and a design manager who reports directly to the managing director (Figure 51). It's because the managing director takes a keen interest in design that these activities are based in the headquarters rather than with engineering and manufacture in Suffolk.

Figure 51 Avent's design team

4.4 Design briefing and concept design

I began the discussion with an examination of how ideas for potential new products come about at Avent. New jobs come into the office via the design manager who gets them in a variety of ways. They may come from an internal idea generated by the design department, the managing director, sales or marketing. Alternatively, ideas can come directly from consumer feedback. All products go out with a small leaflet encouraging people to comment, for which they receive a small gift. These are converted to quarterly reports covering issues such as leakage in a product, capacity limitations, or ideas for new features and these feed into product development. I asked Dawn about this process for converting a problem into a design brief.

> When new jobs come in the three of us sit down and talk about it. We try to put suggestions forward. We'll outline the problem and we may even share some concept ideas. What emerges from these meetings allows us to identify a piece of what we call 'new product development'. Periodically, the MD, sales and marketing directors, technical director and representatives from engineering and tooling get together and we might present ideas at this or they might talk about opportunities for new products. At a recent meeting, the chief executive officer for America attended in order to put a case for some new products she was keen to see in that market.

This filtering process leads to approximately 30–40 new projects each year but of course not all of these will lead to detailed and manufactured products. It's vital that ideas at this stage are converted into a written brief. Such documents form a common point of reference for the many specialist contributions by internal and external staff. (The following quotations are by Dawn Jones unless otherwise stated).

> It reminds people which direction the project should be going in because it's very easy for it to wander as different people add their opinions and knowledge.

The brief might originate in the exchange of e-mail communications or via notes made at a meeting. It may not be very extensive at this stage but it is sufficient to be documented, filed and retrieved by others at any point or used to inform meetings. Changing this briefing document at this early stage is relatively unproblematic and it's important to do so if necessary.

> If there's a change or a suggestion that everybody agrees on, we just change it immediately. It might just mean a little note on the project brief. However, the brief can seem to be leading in a fruitless direction. In this case it must be changed. There's no point following a brief that isn't correct and isn't going where you want to go.

Some of these projects can require very little time – especially where they involve a relatively minor piece of incremental development. However, to create a new product in this field can require anything from one to four years. Within this the concept design will typically take about three to four months. Sufficient time must be left for all the activities in the post-concept phases.

I asked Dawn about her own creativity and how she manages to integrate creative and practical thinking in her work as a designer.

> I like to try and tie down all my constraints and all my main factors first. With our particular products, they all work as a system. Most products will relate together, which might mean some sizes or shapes or materials cannot be altered. Many design decisions are locked, which would seem like a problem but in fact it could be a big help. I sit down with my colleagues and we brainstorm some ideas to see which direction we want to go. I'll make a few rough sketches and from these I will start working on the pre-design.

4.4.1 Feedback on ideas

It's at this stage the design team introduces potential users to provide feedback on conceptual design ideas. Designing for families and young children means there are usually plenty of opportunities to test ideas with employees. As they know the company and understand the need for user feedback employees are usually more inclined to provide detailed opinions. As Dawn points out, 'They are not scared of telling you what they really think about a product'. Not surprisingly, physical models are often the best means of soliciting feedback from users and potential purchasers.

> In one instance we were developing some handles for the small Magic range of plastic drinking cups and we made some basic 3D models. We took these to a nursery and let children play with them, taking photographs of the activity, and this told us a lot about how children held the cups, the acceptability of the size and whether the children liked them.

The designers at Avent have modest model-making facilities of their own in-house. Rigid cellular foam is a particularly popular modelling medium in the design office because it is easily worked to form representations of small and large products (Figure 52). However, the design team quickly move to more robust and visually representative models but these need to be produced by external, professional model makers.

Figure 52 Early concept models of cups and bottles made in rigid cellular foam

Stereolithography has proven itself in allowing designers to convert conceptual ideas generated on computer into tough components that can be assembled to form lifelike 3D representations of new product ideas. These components can also provide the moulds for castings from which can be made highly realistic prototypes that can be used in testing and presentations.

Although this would seem the logical stage at which to bring in technical expertise, Avent tries to involve people from engineering and manufacturing right from the start of a project. Discussions about tooling, for example, might take place alongside the earliest conceptual idea generation. The designers often seek to push established manufacturing techniques into untried territory.

> Quite often, we try to push what kind of product shape can be moulded or explore what a material is capable of. One example appears in the new Sportster cup again [Figure 53]. We originally devised a three-part assembly to create the spout and this matched our conventional moulding processes. Unfortunately this resulted in a split line right across where the valve sits, which obviously could lead to problems of leakage. Interestingly, in our user trials, some mothers indicated that the parts of the cup were fiddly to assemble. So we were pushing for a long time to get the engineering department to use a two-shot moulding process, where two different types of plastic are injected into the mould at two stages thereby making one component that has different properties in different parts – in this case part flexible, part rigid. Admittedly this is a lot more complicated. It took quite a bit of persuasion and development but eventually together, we found a way of doing it. The Sportster cup is now in production. [The two-shot moulding process is discussed in more detail later.]

Figure 53 Avent Sportster drinking bottle – a recent introduction (2003)

4.4.2 Computer-aided design at Avent

This course has highlighted the vital use of computers in modern design practice. Much of Dawn's day-to-day activity is now computer based.

> I would estimate 70 per cent of my work now takes place at a computer. When I first started design about 12 years ago, perhaps about 5 per cent of my work was on computer. It has totally changed. I rely totally on the computer these days. We go into three-dimensional CAD very early in the design process, mostly using ProEngineer and SolidWorks. I use these from the conceptual stage right through to detail design. Of course, you have to build the models a slightly different way to that required by the production people, which requires a process of translation, but if you understand these constraints it is possible to use these CAD programmes very early on.

So in theory the same CAD model can be passed down through an organisation for each department to work with, leading ideally to the use of these CAD models in the production of tooling for manufacture. But in practice many CAD models need to be remade at the end of the design stage because the requirements of production are different to the requirements of design. For example, the detail design of components requires the definition of tolerances that are unnecessary at the earlier design stages. Also, some production systems require specific types of CAD models that would be unwieldy to use for conceptual design.

4.5 Product analysis: Magic Sportster

Avent recently developed and launched the Magic Sportster drinking bottle aimed at the toddler market (twelve months and older). This product originally came about via consumer responses from the UK and US markets. The company already manufactures a small, 207 ml bottle with a soft spout aimed at children in the three-months-plus age group. In response to customer feedback the Sportster offers a larger, 340 ml capacity. The larger cup has a deliberately less babyish identity.

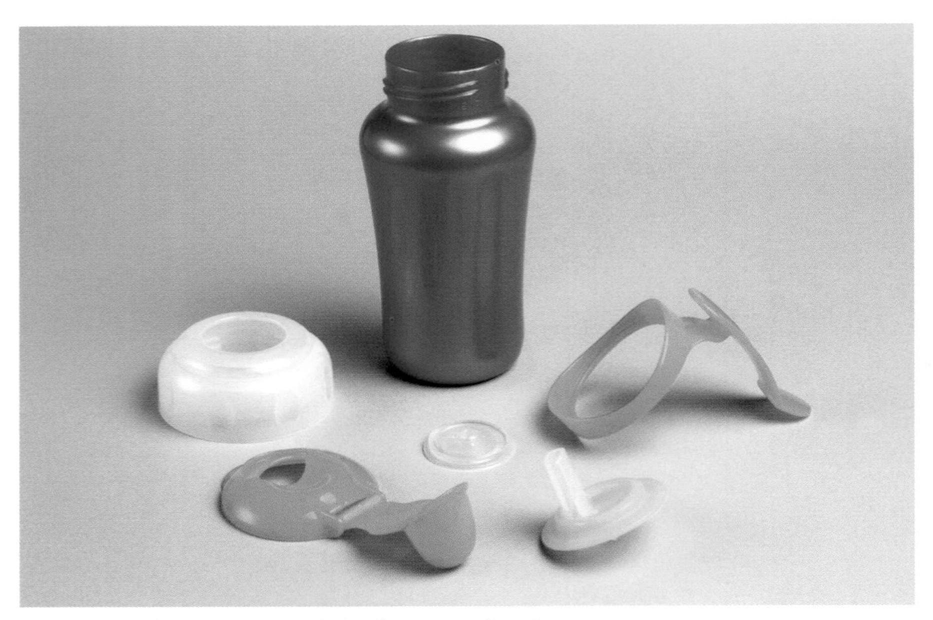

Figure 54 Components of the Sportster bottle

> At the outset of this project our main constraints were: (a) it had to look okay within the existing product range, and (b) it had to be compatible with screw fittings in the rest of the range, therefore allowing components to be interchangeable [Figure 54]. There are clear economies from our point of view because handles from other products can be used on the new product but it also means it's very easy for a parent to mix and match parts. Clearly, this constrained us quite heavily. Also we wanted all products to work with other components in the wider Avent system, such as the bottle warmer. We explored stretching the cup, making it wider, but all the time conscious of the shot capacities of our injection and blow moulding machines in Suffolk. The creative development was informed by how many we needed to produce in a year, the machines we would use, limitations on tool size, shot weight and the particular plastic selected for the job. Our materials options are very limited because all our cups have to be sterilisable and many are put into microwave ovens for warming drinks. Each cup uses approximately 60 cc of plastic and we are making about 3 million per year.

Figure 55 Early 3D studies that were influential in the Sportster project

The Sportster cup didn't begin entirely with consumer feedback from the smaller version. It was influenced by some earlier speculative experiments that had been tried and shelved about a year earlier. These earlier experiments were more conceptual studies of tumbler-type drinking vessels for children that did not rely on screw threads to hold components together (Figure 55).

> We went back to the original, earlier project and tried to lift some details that we were quite proud of but hadn't actually managed to put through to production. A few of these were obviously of benefit to the consumer such as the stem and the valves, which exploited the two-shot moulding technology I mentioned earlier. In doing this it was vital that the new valve was compatible with cups across the whole system – again the importance of interchangeability. This is a very good example of a part that was designed very closely with engineering and tooling because there were so many limitations on the spacing of components.

Figure 56 Sportster spout made using a two-shot moulding process

Figure 57 Sportster lid mechanism

4.5.1 Two-shot moulding process

In the two-shot moulding process the moulding tool actually contains two moulds and the whole assembly rotates around a centre. In the first stage the hard polymer is moulded first. A material such as polypropylene is heated and injected into the mould. Part of the mould opens to allow this moulding to be lifted out, the tool rotates, the moulding is inserted back into the mould but this time a new larger cavity is present. The second shot involves the injection of a different, softer polymer that is deposited only in particular places on the first moulding. Where the two polymers touch they bond together, forming a tough and durable single component but that has two different characteristics (Figure 56). The moulding can be bent and twisted but the two materials won't come apart.

I asked Dawn Jones about the use of this two-shot moulding process in the Sportster cup.

> There were a lot of potential production problems and we had to liaise very closely with tooling. We used some existing parts while other parts were newly designed – partly to give the product a more grown up feel. The flip-top lid is a two-part assembly but we did look at a single moulding that incorporated an integral plastic hinge [Figure 57]. However, we were worried about the life of this product and although such hinges can have a long life this one had to take enormous abuse with children and we decided to play safe. Our design also meant we could have a nice snap-open feature for which we would not have to pay a licence fee. Almost all integral plastic hinges that have a flip feature are licensed. It would have added a few pennies on to the cost price, which, by the time it gets to the consumer, adds quite a lot on to the price.

4.5.2 Other design considerations

But the moulding issues were only one group among a host of conflicting and competing design considerations.

> The design team was keen that this flip-top lid had a very tactile quality – the product should be like a gadget for children to play with. We wanted this to be apparent to the directors when they reviewed the proposals – to see the fun in the action. But we didn't lose sight that the product also had to offer interchangeability with other products, that it had to accept both the original and new spouts in the opening.
>
> And there's still further development to do. The flip isn't exactly as we intended it. We really wanted it to flip open as soon as any pressure was applied. We managed to get our models to function like this but it was difficult to achieve when engineered. The speed of the project also limited the time that could be spent honing this feature.

The Sportster cup reveals some very subtle features based on perceptions of user wants and preferences – particularly considering the product needs to appeal to children (the users) and their parents or carers (the purchasers). Perceptions of the market have led to some very extensive and sophisticated design development work, which in turn has generated product features that differentiate this product from its competitors. The interchangeability across drinking cups in the Avent range is an important marketing device. It's advantages such as these that get a product accepted in a company and sent through to production.

The manufacturing cost incurred by companies is usually classified as commercially sensitive information and few firms are prepared to divulge their costs. The processes of working out the selling price for any given consumer product can differ widely between companies. As you saw in Block 2 the primary aim is to ensure price is greater than cost. Some companies simply establish the price a market is prepared to pay for a product and then work backwards from this to see if they can develop a suitable product that will retail at or below this price. Given the number of components and the metallic colours used in the body, I estimate the Sportster cup costs about £0.70 to make. Apparently the original master batches turned out to be expensive and a lot of extra development work was required to bring the price down.

4.6 Injection moulding process

4.6.1 Manufacturing costs

Figure 58 Sportster cup (left) shown next to a pre-form (right)

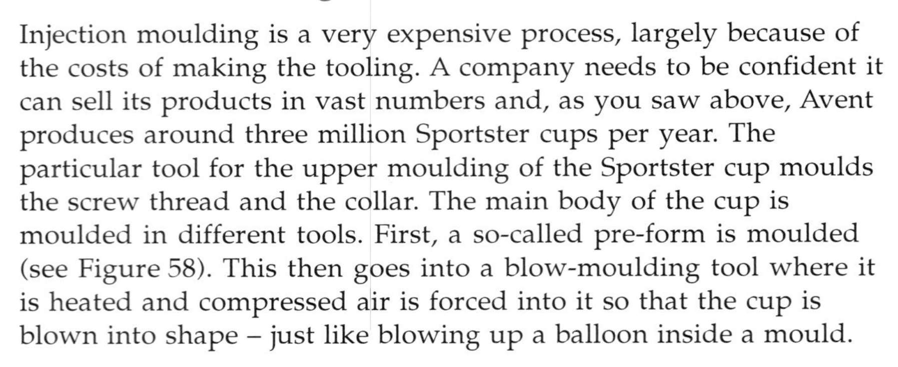

Injection moulding is a very expensive process, largely because of the costs of making the tooling. A company needs to be confident it can sell its products in vast numbers and, as you saw above, Avent produces around three million Sportster cups per year. The particular tool for the upper moulding of the Sportster cup moulds the screw thread and the collar. The main body of the cup is moulded in different tools. First, a so-called pre-form is moulded (see Figure 58). This then goes into a blow-moulding tool where it is heated and compressed air is forced into it so that the cup is blown into shape – just like blowing up a balloon inside a mould.

Such machines can easily cost a quarter of a million pounds with additional tooling costs of £150 000 for some components but a company would expect to run the machine and tools almost 24 hours a day for up to five years without significant repair or development time.

Companies make as few changes as possible to the moulds and associated tooling during the development process. Ideally the tooling will be 'right first time' but in practice when the first mouldings come off the mould tool and are evaluated something requires improvement and frequently many things need minor modifications. Each modification will probably mean removing small amounts of steel from the mould tool or, in particularly serious cases, putting metal back onto the mould. Both of these require high precision tools and expertise and consequently it is very expensive. Also, the more times you tweak an injection mould, the weaker you make it – especially if it involves welding.

> Because of these costs we try and get it right first time – mainly by making an awful lot of models. We spend a lot of money up-front on stereolithography models just to try and prove things very early on. But even then, sometimes you find problems after the tooling is made.

4.6.2 Prototyping

I've touched on some of the rapid prototyping used by Avent and I wanted to explore this further.

> We use several processes. Fusion deposition modelling (FDM) is one process we frequently use. This is a layering process using a nylon or ABS material. The components made by FDM are immensely strong. We can really throw the models around and put them through their functional paces. At the conceptual stage we might have resin models made that give a good representation of the overall form but they are more fragile. They are really just visual models. They can be handled but they mustn't come into contact with water so they can't be used in real drinking trials.

Polyurethane resin models are made by making a flexible silicon mould from a master SLA model. This mould is then injected with liquid resin and allowed to cure after which the flexible silicon mould can be peeled away to reveal the new model – in this case a model of the cup. As the resins come in a variety of colours and finishes the model can be quite lifelike. The only real problem with resin models is they aren't safe to evaluate in user trials with potential users. You can show people and they can feel them and comment on the visual qualities but designers need to go to other techniques such as FDM if they need to create robust and usable models.

> If we do need to model something for actually feeding or drinking, we will get some prototype tools made by stereolithography using a composite of polymer and metal or get mould tools made in aluminium. These tools are usually relatively cheap to make because the materials are much softer but they are good enough to get a couple of hundred mouldings off. We use these for consumer trials. I can think of one product in particular where results from consumer trials led us to make a complete change to the concept of the product. Initially, it wasn't what the market wanted at all.

As you have seen, Avent uses the services of outside model makers and rapid prototypers. Computer files generated by the design department at Avent are transferred via the Internet to the particular modelling company selected; Avent has developed such good working relationships that this is just like sending files to an internal department.

4.7 Design beyond production

Specialist consultants will sometimes be responsible for the way a product is seen in the shops and on the Internet but in certain companies this can be merely another aspect of in-house design. At Avent, designing for so-called point-of-sale is increasingly being considered from the outset of projects. This might involve the packaging of the product, supporting graphics and even the in-store display.

> In some projects we have felt the traditional types of packaging have been not very suitable for our products. Some packages allow a product to be tampered with or do not protect it properly in transit. We have to take responsibility for this and so we spend time on designing the point-of-sale packaging.

Often, potential customers will be exposed to the image of a product well before they get to examine and use it. Much of this image is created by the way it is presented and packaging has an important role here. Clever design can link the identity of the product to the identity of the packaging thereby creating the impression of a unified and organised company. Packaging also offers other possibilities for unifying products across a diverse range. And it should be noted that retailers want product packaging to look as attractive as possible because it makes their job easier.

Of course, as noted in the quote above, one of the primary aims of packaging is to protect the product – perhaps from accidental damage or deliberate tampering but given this can be achieved then an important secondary aim is to increase the appeal of the product in a cost-effective way.

Figure 59 Avent Sportster (left) and Trainer cups (right) in new polypropylene hanging packs

The packaging designed for the Magic Trainer and Magic Sportster cups' seals, protects and promotes the products in a very cost effective way. It is a good example of how to achieve the aim with the minimum of materials. The packaging keeps the lids securely in place so buyers can be confident about hygiene; both packs protect the important areas around the lids and drinking nozzles but don't try to protect the stronger cup bodies or bases, and both packs offer a large surface area for publicity images, information and instructions. Figure 59 shows a new polypropylene hanging pack that wraps around the product and is held in place with a heat weld.

> The original concept for these packs was developed here but we need to liaise a lot with our packaging people to check that what we are proposing is viable. Clearly there are many different products in the range and we try to find one design that will encompass the whole range. The design must be compatible with the need to present information in different languages but usually this is simply a matter of translating instructions and perhaps slightly changing the artwork, which is done by an outside graphic consultancy.

4.8 Product analysis: Express steam steriliser

4.8.1 Current version

The Avent brand covers a range of products and I was keen to explore one of the more technological products in contrast to the simpler bottles. The Express steam steriliser was originally launched in 1987 and has proved to be a successful product in the range (Figure 60). It was designed to sterilise six Avent feeding bottles in eight minutes. Users add exactly 90 ml of tap water and the intensive heat generated in the product kills all household germs. It can also be used with other Avent products such as teats where sterilisation is required and it will probably be used by parents and carers of babies up to six months old. The product has recently returned to the design office for some updating. The design team are exploring the fitting of an indicator that informs users about the sterilisation cycle. The new product will have the name IQ.

Figure 60 Early version of Express electric steam steriliser

At present the product exploits a basic electrical steriliser that consists of a heating element pressed into a dyecast housing and controlled by a thermostat. Users activate the heating element and the steriliser simply heats up until the thermostat switches, at which point the contents have been exposed to four minutes of sterilisation via the boiling water. The whole process, including warming up and cooling down, takes about twelve minutes and therein lies the opportunity for development. Dawn Jones provided the background to this project.

> The product in its current form has been on the market for several years so it is in need of a bit of a face-lift. It was a project we fancied tackling but it wasn't until a new engineer joined the company that some early ideas could be developed. This engineer had expertise in electronics so with his help, we worked out what improvements we could make while

retaining the existing body of the product. We came up with a basic heating control cycle and had the electronics prototyped [Figures 61 and 62]. This told us how much internal space would be required. From that, we devised a little display that fitted the existing body and quickly produced some models and working prototypes. It probably took a couple of months in total. We wanted to surprise people here before they knew about the project.

The display panel is retained in the body of the steriliser by using existing moulding posts found on the inside of the casing [Figure 63]. The new display literally slots into place. The product uses all the existing elements such as the heater and thermostat but offers users a new level of control and it informs users of the state of its sterilisation cycle. We've not added much to the cost but there's lots of added value. We presented the idea at a new products development meeting and it was very much liked [Figure 64].

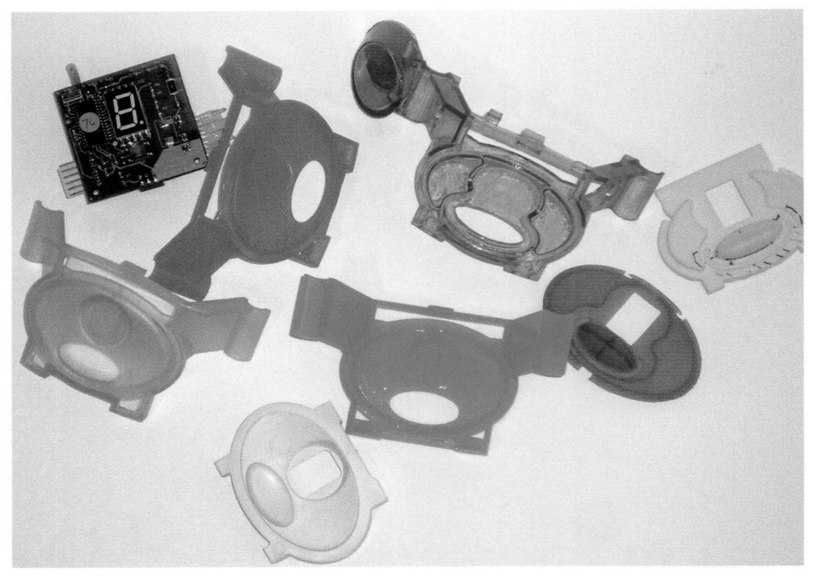

Figure 61 Range of prototyped components to assess form, fit and colour

Figure 62 Avent IQ steriliser prototype components. The control electronics fit in the oval aperture.

Figure 63 Prototype control unit fitted to the steriliser body

Figure 64 CAD visualisation of the new steriliser

4.8.2 New steriliser

The new version of the steriliser retains all the functionality of its predecessor but it provides distinct user benefits. It cuts down the time for sterilisation because the sensors detect the amount of water in the unit and the temperatures in use. For most users the cycle time is reduced from the previous twelve minutes to eight minutes. The same timer electronics are programmed to provide users with the time that has elapsed since the sterilisation process came to an end, because in theory items should be resterilised if they have been left standing in the unit for longer than three hours.

Usability and the improvement of the user experience was one of the key drivers in this example of development. The electronic controller offered the design team many new opportunities but each one also gave rise to potential misunderstandings or misuse by the consumer. Much of the design activity concerned retaining the desired features while minimising the opportunities for user error. Figures 61–63 show some of the 3D models and prototypes made during development. Figure 63 is a prototype moulding of the casing with the control panel clipped in place from behind.

The company arranged for the production version of the circuit board to be made by an outside contractor even though all the prototyping was done in-house. The main reason for this is the very thorough testing that must take place on such consumer products – especially considering the high humidity and high working temperature of the product. The electronic circuitry is protected from the vapour and temperature by silicon seals between the steriliser unit and the dyecast chassis, but European standards dictate that all products must pass a series of tests designed to evaluate performance under various severe conditions.

The development programme also allowed the design department to offer some refreshment to some of the colours used in the product. It would have been very expensive to stop one production line and run off some alternative colour versions, so during development these components were made by the external model makers using vacuum casting and other rapid-prototyping techniques.

As you saw in the essay by Evans in the *Modelling Workbook* some of these techniques require a model maker to rub down the raw components until their surfaces are smooth. These are then used to make a flexible silicon mould, probably with two halves. Into this is injected the resin that will become the tough model that can be used on the working model or prototype. Care needs to be taken in the choice of modelling material because some of these resins start to soften at around 50°C – particularly important when prototyping a product that brings water up to boiling point. Other resins can withstand heat but may not represent colour accurately.

4.9 Design communication

This study has confirmed that a great deal of design communication needs to take place in the development of products – particularly between the design office and the external model makers. Much of the simple communication can exploit e-mail and the telephone but the sharing of CAD files is now almost as common.

As you saw in Block 5, design drawings and CAD models are saved as STL files and sent as attachments to e-mail messages. These files are compressed to make them smaller, easier to handle and faster to send. Once received these files are decompressed and can be uploaded to the various rapid-prototyping machines as necessary.

> I really don't know what we did before file sharing and rapid-prototyping. Yes I do, we sent off drawings and it took us weeks to get the models back. Now I can send a file and two days later I get the stereolithography addition model. We check this over, send it back for finishing and casting, and five days later we can be having our first trials with a prototype.

The new steriliser (see Figure 64) was launched at a major baby product exhibition in Dallas in May 2003 and the UK launch took place in September of that year. It's not easy for companies to determine how a product will be received and how successful it might be. In the case of the steriliser there is an additional cost when compared to the original model but because this is a high-value product it was anticipated that the market would accept this. At the time of writing (2004), Avent plans to retail both the old and new models side by side in outlets such as Boots in order to generate some consumer feedback.

4.10 Design for manufacture

As noted above, manufacturing is considered as early as possible, certainly in the concept design stage. At the earliest new product development meetings, the engineering and manufacturing director is present to raise questions regarding, for example, the kind of production line set-ups that might be required. He needs to know he has space in his factory to be able to produce the types of products the designer is proposing. Some reorganisation may be required.

With reference to the Sportster cup, the design team was liaising with the toolmakers almost from the outset of the project – particularly concerning the spout components and the two-shot moulding process (Figure 65). Other components required little collaboration regarding design for manufacture because they closely resembled existing items for which the production problems had been solved.

Figure 65 Sportster spout. Vacuum cast models (top); production samples (bottom).

4.10.1 Teamworking

Clearly, design at Avent is a process of teamworking. There are small, localised teams, for example the teams in the design office, and wider teams involving, for example, the external model makers, the printed circuit board manufacturers or the testers.

> I believe teamworking is essential in design. Nobody has the expertise to cover every aspect. In this company some projects require only a few people and you tend to pull on resources as you need them. Other projects require bigger teams. We normally have an engineer assigned to a project – someone from production. We don't tend to have one person who champions a particular project throughout its design and development as some companies do. When it goes into the production phase, when it's signed off from concept to go through to production, it will be assigned an engineer and they will hold the technical file and all the documentation. They have responsibility for it then.

4.10.2 Commercial constraints

The commercial environment within which design operates today puts some severe pressures on companies and particularly those responsible for the design and development of products. There are pressures not only to get things right – to make sure products are safe and reliable for the user and economic for the manufacturer – but also to get things right first time, that is, to minimise the time and costs of development. The use of CAD and the ability to share digital files has had a major influence here because it has removed some of the processes of interpretation required in traditional product development processes.

> We use a variety of software including ProEngineer but as I mentioned earlier some CAD data are remade in the move from design to production. The requirements of the design modelling may differ from the requirements needed by production staff. For example, we may want a programme that allows rapid changing of components and we're prepared to sacrifice engineering accuracy for this. Whereas production engineers will usually want to specify exact dimensions and tolerances and can be confident the concept will not change radically. It's two very different requirements and we sometimes use different computer programmes to achieve this. In some respects it reflects two different ways of thinking.

Today the concept design phase can involve a consideration of tooling as much as the form and image of the product. The easy and rapid generation of 3D models provides a means for the designer and toolmaker to engage in discussions about the requirements of a particular piece of development, even where this is supplemented with detailed 2D CAD drawings.

I asked Dawn if she found this responsibility to consider manufacture at the same time as the concept, usability and marketing a bit of a straitjacket on her creative design thinking.

> It's not a restriction and it doesn't mean I have to compromise on design. There are ways and means around even the most difficult production problems and I like using my creativity to overcome mismatches between the concept design we want and the restrictions of materials or processes we have to work with. You just have to think about problems slightly differently.

4.11 Sustainability

I asked Dawn if the pressures and responsibilities towards sustainability were apparent to her in the markets that Avent operates within.

> It's very much more evident in Europe than say, in the States. In the States they really have a different outlook. In recent times, we have tried to get the most out of one particular part – we would try to reuse a component or, alternatively, reduce the amount of material in a component or make something recyclable. But in the development work we've done for the American market this doesn't seem to be so much of a priority. They seem to have a different mindset. In fact, the two-shot moulding process I talked about earlier is unhelpful in this respect because it makes recovery and separation of the two materials very difficult. It provides wonderful design advantages but recycling is really bad. But we are trying to act responsibly by using it only when it offers the consumer a real advantage.
>
> The influence of legislation regarding recycling and recoverability has not had a major effect in the company so far but we are trying to keep ahead of the game. The larger, electrical products such as the steriliser present the most difficult problems for us. It's very difficult trying to make products for different markets around the world, each with different forms of legislation.

4.12 Quality control

Avent is in an advantageous commercial position. It has a good market lead for many of its products in the babycare sector and it operates with high standards of quality control – not just in production but also in design. Avent would rather pull the plug on a design project rather than let an imperfect design out on to the market where it might tarnish the reputation of the brand. But when it does decide to go with a design proposal the pressure is on.

> At the moment we are working on a project that's been in the background for a couple of years. Suddenly, it's been decided the concept is right and the time is right. We've got six months to turn our project round and that is very tight for us.

In society now there is the strong possibility of litigation and products must be checked not only by the company but also by the relevant standards organisations to ensure they are as safe as possible. I asked Dawn how quality and product safety are checked.

> The company keeps very good records, from both the concept design and the stages after this. We ensure all our design work is documented; all testing is documented, as are the discussions at project reviews. We try and do a failure modes and effects analysis [usually abbreviated to FMEA] on projects and products where there may be any sort of risks for the end user. But the main testing really takes place when the concept moves into engineering and detail development. We have quite a large quality department within the company that continually tests new and established products. For example, with the sterilisers, I believe a certain number of samples are taken off the production line everyday. There is a little room that is basically just boiling sterilisers just to check the kind of variances we get on things. They sample the bottles, the teats, all those sorts of products. Some products we might want to test to destruction.

Tests such as these are invaluable to design and companies must ensure there are effective channels for test results to be fed back to product design and development. At Avent, the use of regular product reviews allows results from testing to be fed back into the development loop. These product review meetings, like the design review meetings, provide an opportunity for a variety of personnel to comment on emerging issues or problems, and for plans to be made to rectify a problem with a product.

Today you are likely to find Avent products in many high street retailers, out-of-town warehouses and on the Internet. As the patents run out on the early product designs so design quality becomes more important in order for Avent to maintain its market lead.

Case study 5
Minds Eye computer games

5.1 Introduction

Figure 66 Promotion graphic from Minds Eye's website

This case study looks at designing within a company called Minds Eye. The company is located in Milton Keynes and develops computer games. The product of the design activity is almost entirely electronic, apart from the disk and case that it is sold in. This provides a contrast to the other case studies where the output of the design process is a tangible product. You will see however that the design processes have many similarities. It is also important to realise the design of software is intrinsically linked to the development of electronic hardware. An increasing number of products depend on the bringing together of software and hardware. This case study provides an insight into the process of designing software interfaces in the highly graphic world of computer games.

5.2 Company background

Managing director, Martin Batten, started Minds Eye Productions in 1995 with financial backing from a UK software publishing company. Martin Batten's background in graphic design, coupled with an interest in computer gaming led to an interest in developing products to meet the growing demand for computer games. Creating animations for broadcasters has always been another part of the company's business (Figure 67); for example the company designed the graphics for the television programme *Robot Wars*.

Figure 67 Scene from Hardy Perennial Pizza, an animation developed for the BBC

Minds Eye now designs games for all kinds of entertainment media, including games for touch screen kiosks in bars and for mobile phones. However, the company's main design efforts are currently focused on two areas: the development of games for computers and consoles such as PlayStation and Xbox, and games for interactive television.

Figure 68 Pacman: Adventures in Time

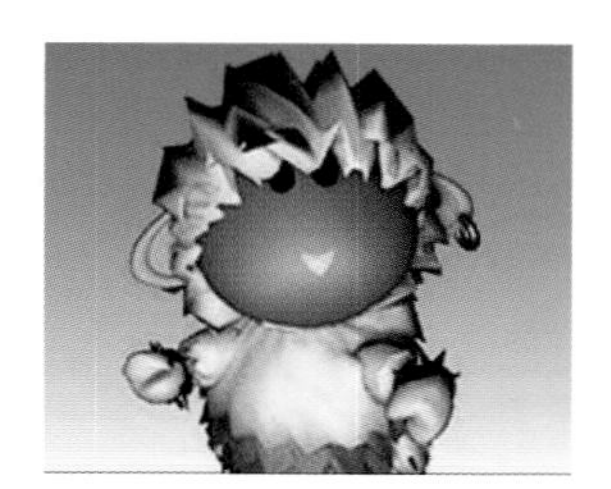

Figure 69 Sheep

Figure 70 Monopoly

The evolving nature of the technology means computer games have a life of between three and five years. Well-known PC and console games by Minds Eye include Pacman: Adventures in Time, Sheep and Monolpoly (Figures 68–70). New games are frequently launched by the software publishers using advertising, publicity campaigns and press reviews. As a game ages the price usually drops until finally towards the end of its life it ends up in the bargain buckets. Some games though are reworked into new formats, for example Sheep, which was originally a PC and console game, has now been relaunched for the Game Boy Advance.

Box 1 What do computer games do?

If you have not played computer games, you may be wondering what they do.

There are some common features of games.

- All games have an objective, something you have to achieve. This may be collecting things on the way to a particular destination or surviving the attacks of malevolent characters or it may be something more intellectual like answering questions correctly.
- All games also have some form of scoring to tell you how well you are doing at achieving your objective. This may be in different forms, for example points you earn, or some kind of virtual reward like money.
- Most games have different levels of complexity, which enable the player to progress as they become more skilled.
- Many games have an avatar, a character who represents you and from whose perspective you see the game.

5.2.1 Developing new games

Companies such as Minds Eye are developers. The games it makes are sold through software publishers, much as an author writes for a publishing house.

The development of games is inextricably linked to the development of the hardware on which they will be played. As the technology of computing has advanced and new possibilities have opened up, the complexity of games has increased. For example, the development of 3D video acceleration has made it possible to design increasingly realistic 3D worlds in games. As the hardware develops more is demanded of games, which has led to increasingly large numbers of people being involved in the design of new games. In the early days of gaming two people would work on a game. Now, at Minds Eye a team of 20 people work on each game and in some larger software companies the numbers are far greater. Martin Batten anticipates that in the future these numbers will increase still further perhaps by a factor of 10.

5.2.2 Interactive television

In addition to its work on computer games Minds Eye is one of only a handful of companies in the UK making games for the medium of interactive television. At the time of writing in 2004, this fairly new medium is more developed in Britain than anywhere else in the world. The UK lead is due to the effective monopoly of the broadcaster BSkyB in the interactive TV medium. This situation has enabled the development of both content and services in a way that has not happened in other countries where there is greater competition and the share of the market is smaller.

Interactive television gaming is many years behind computer gaming technically because of the limitations of the hardware, and the design of games is closer to the early days of computer games than the current state of the art. However, it has been found that interactive television games are played by equal numbers of women and men, with the majority of female players playing games during the daytime. This is attributed to two things: a greater number of puzzle games such as word games and spatial games such as Tetris, and ease of access and payment. The 'micropayments' for games can now be made at the touch of a button. Minds Eye anticipates that interactive gaming will grow in popularity.

Minds Eye used to take on lots of small projects but now it concentrates on a few medium-size ones and the more manageable interactive TV games. Only the biggest companies in the games industry have enough resources to have several major projects running simultaneously. For a small company like Minds Eye there is always a tension between looking for new business and the next contract and the demands of finishing the project in hand. The last three months of any project are always the busiest but that is also the time when there is the most need to search out the next contract.

5.3 Computer games industry

The games industry is one of the largest of all of the electronic entertainment industries. This relatively young industry initially comprised many small developers; as the industry has matured, however, some of these developers have gone out of business and there are now fewer companies in the industry. In 2003 in the UK the number of game development companies went from 400 to about 300 and this trend looks set to continue. The publishers who previously outsourced all development work are now hiring staff made redundant by game developers to create their own in-house development teams.

The games industry is dominated by young men, many of whom have been playing computer games since they were very young. The consequences of this are that the number of games designed to appeal specifically to girls is very limited and the majority of sales are to boys and young men.

In the UK in 2003, 50 million games were sold with a market value of £1.7 billion.

Of the games sold a handful (5 per cent) make 95 per cent of the industry's profits. Large international publishers such as Electronic

Arts (15 per cent market share) and Sony (7 per cent market share) are growing while smaller publishers' fortunes depend upon the reviews and consequent sales of individual games.

5.4 How games are commissioned

Computer games are commissioned by the software publisher who either approaches developers such as Minds Eye directly or invites companies to tender. The publisher has a brief for the game it is proposing, but the detail in this can vary. Some briefs are a two-page outline of what the game is to be based on and what features it should have. Other publishers offer a more detailed specification that gives background detail and information the games developers can incorporate into their proposals.

Often, games require the developers to obtain a license from the rights holders of particular characters. The games industry tries to anticipate trends in the movie industry so as to develop topical games that will coincide with the release of movies. There are also games based around classic favourites, particularly for children. Minds Eye has made games around characters such as Lara Croft, Noddy, Thomas the Tank Engine and Starsky and Hutch.

Three or four companies may be invited to tender and asked to say how they would develop the game proposed by the publisher. Minds Eye often only has two weeks to put such a proposal together. A design proposal for tender will be an illustrated document outlining the proposed games, its characters and all of the settings, scenes and interactive objects that will appear in the game. These are the basic components of the game. Minds Eye sometimes also mocks up a demo of the game using existing but similar story engines (a story engine is the software that drives the game). The Minds Eye team may also mock up reviews of the potential game to make it seem more real.

The design proposal has to make sense in terms of design, technical development and commercial feasibility. The proposal also needs to be realistic; there is no sense in promising features that are graphically or technically impossible or too costly to implement. Usually the response to proposals is quick, it may be as short as a week, but sometimes the company has to wait up to three months to know whether its proposal has been accepted. Even then things can change a lot depending on the fortunes of the related movie and the gaming industry at large.

Occasionally, Minds Eye itself comes up with an idea that it tries to interest publishers in. In this case it draws up a proposal and mocks up the software to show the idea. One of the company's most successful games, Sheep, was proposed by staff at Minds Eye rather than a publisher. Some of the images below come from the proposal for a game called Paparazzi that was put together to interest publishers (Figure 71). This shows how graphics are used at this very early stage to convey not only information but also a feel for how the game might look and play. The written proposal, which these graphics illustrate, describes the storyline and then goes on to describe the elements of the game.

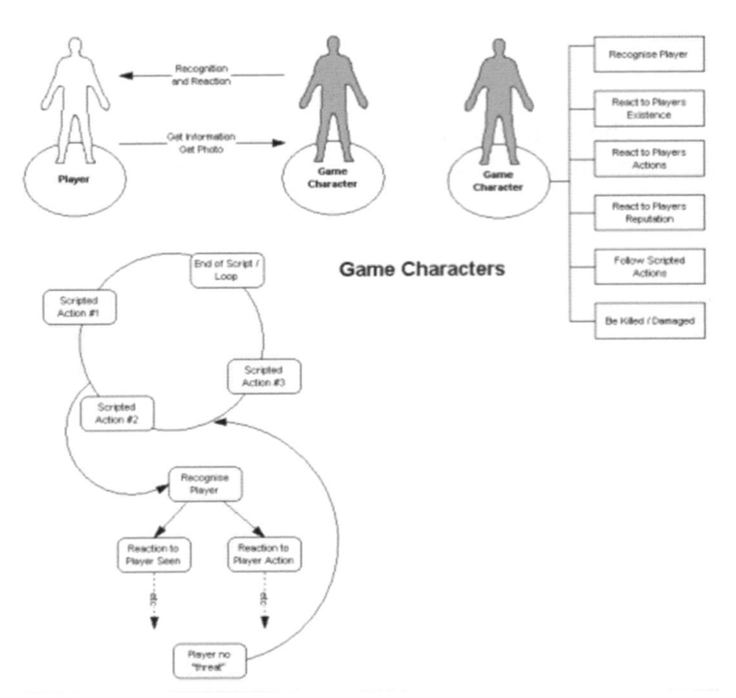

(a) Exploring character

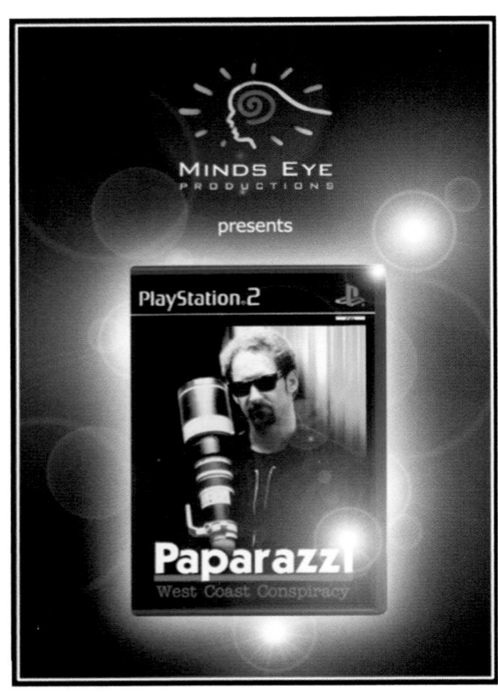

(b) Mock up of CD cover

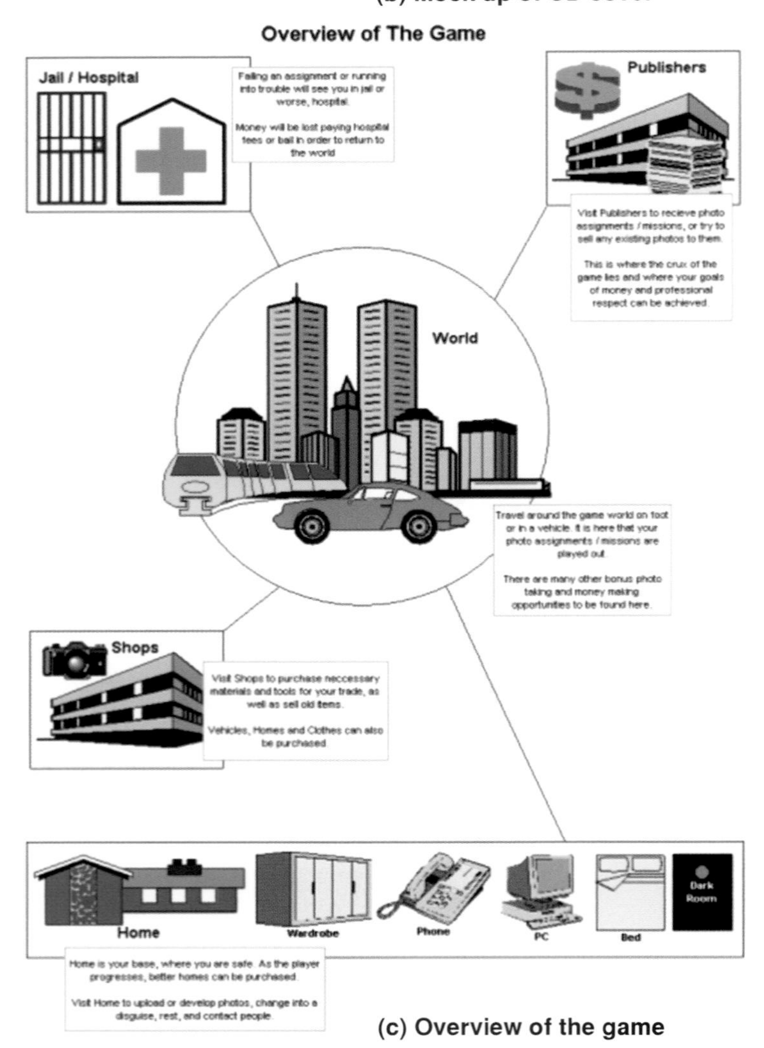

(c) Overview of the game

Figure 71 Graphics from the proposal for a new game titled Paparazzi

Once the company is commissioned the publisher appoints an external producer who will monitor the project – getting to know the people involved and the design and technology, inputting ideas and liaising with the whole team. There are also monthly milestones, targets to be achieved. It is important this relationship with the external producer works well or is at least satisfactory. At Minds Eye this relationship has only failed on a couple of occasions and in both instances the external producer was eventually replaced.

The development of a computer or console game usually takes between one year and two and a half years and involves a team of 20 people. For interactive television the development of games, takes anything from six weeks to five months and involves only one or two people depending on the complexity of the game. Most of the interactive TV games that Minds Eye has developed have taken about three months to complete (Figure 72).

(a) BeeHive

(b) Banzai

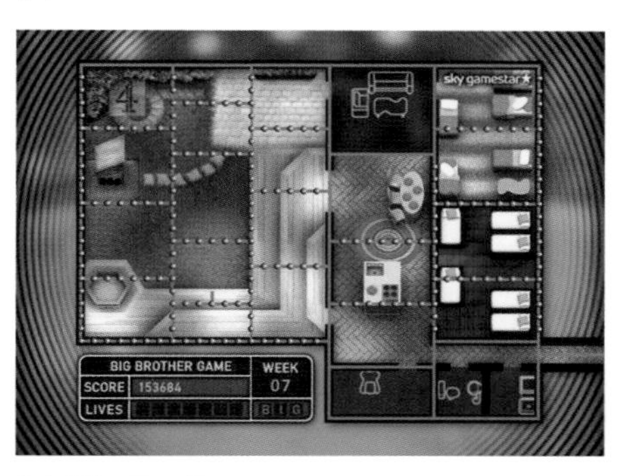

(c) Big Brother

Figure 72 Screenshots from interactive TV games

These development times reflect the money these products will make. BSkyB, for whom the interactive games are developed, has a library of games and individual games are rotated or churned through the library every so often to get new players. However, some of the more popular games like Who Wants to be a Millionaire, Monopoly and Tetris have a long life and are permanently in the BSkyB library. The aim of both broadcaster and developer is to develop games that customers will return to frequently.

5.4.1 Degree of freedom

Minds Eye, as a software developer, is answerable to the software publisher that has commissioned the product. This inevitably places some constraints on the design of games. Occasionally there will be problems to do with changing requirements of the publisher. For example, during the development of the game Starsky and Hutch the publisher saw some games at an exhibition that were attractive. The publisher then asked for changes to be made to the game, which was already in development. This led to a two-month hold up while the external producer and the development team discussed the feasibility of the suggested changes. Eventually most of the suggested changes were not included as it was realised these features would completely alter the concept of the game.

On another occasion a large project for an American corporation collapsed when that company was bought out and lost the licensing rights for the character that was central to the product Minds Eye was working on.

5.5 Design process

5.5.1 Who is involved?

There are three main categories of staff working on a game: artists, game designers and coders. For each project there is a lead artist, designer and coder and these people work closely with the internal producer who manages the whole project. The game publisher also appoints the external producer whose role is to oversee the project and safeguard the publisher's interests.

Each group involved has its own specific responsibilities.

- The artists are responsible for developing the 3D graphics and the look of the game.
- The game designers design how the game is played at each level of complexity.
- The coders do the programming necessary to make all this happen.

Box 2 Dean the artist and Ben the game designer

Dean is a lead artist; he is a self-taught computer game fanatic who spent most of his adolescence learning how to create 3D computer graphics. He now teaches students at Ravensbourne College of Art how to use Maya software. Dean started work producing computer graphics for a road surfacing company and then moved to Minds Eye where he has created sequences for the television series *Robot Wars* and a 3D computer pet series as well as several games.

Ben originally trained in 3D graphics and animation but as a consummate gamer became more interested in designing the game play. Ben believes, 'games need to be designed so that the player feels that when he fails it is not the fault of the game design but their own lack of skill. It is important the game feels fair'. As lead designer Ben feels it is important to retain a vision of the game throughout the development process.

5.5.2 Starting the design

Projects usually begin with a small team from each group of staff putting together a concept document that is used to create the design proposal at the tendering stage. The concept document usually contains details of the main story line for the game, the game's rules, the functionality of the game, the camera angles, components and characters. This is a lengthy, illustrated document that considers the concept from the points of view of graphic design, game play and software encoding. At the concept stage the Minds Eye team is concerned with whether its proposal is feasible. Can the artists create all the characters and components required in the time available? Is the game playable and engaging and can the functionality be coded in?

The finalised concept document is passed to the managing director who uses it as the basis of the design proposal that can be submitted to the commissioning publisher.

The level of detail in the design proposal is high. For example, the design proposal document for the game Starsky and Hutch is 74 pages long and contains many illustrations including specially commissioned 2D pictures of characters (Figures 73 and 74), screenshots and diagrams of different functions and structures. An example of the level of detail this proposal contains can be seen in Figure 75.

Figure 73 Sketch drawn by a freelance graphic artist at the start of the Starsky and Hutch project

Figure 74 Drawing of Starsky for the design document

Design proposal: roads

Starsky and Hutch 2 will contain similar roads to that found in the first game. There will be a number of changes to the roads that will provide better game play features as well as more variety. There will be eight different classes of road.

Class	Road type	Description
free	freeway	A wide and fast-moving road. There will be proper American-style, cloverleaf junctions taking you on and off the freeway, along with junctions linking freeways together.
A	primary road	The most commonly used road. It comprises of a pavement, a parking lane, a single carriageway and a central reservation. The central reservation will be used to house flowerbeds, tram lanes, pillars, road works, and other such features.
B	secondary road	This road is very similar to the A road but will not contain a central reservation.
C	urban road	This road will be used within any urban areas of the city. It comprises of a pavement and single carriageway.
D	alleyway	The alleyways will be slightly wider than those used in the first Starsky and Hutch game in order to reduce the chances of vehicles getting stuck. There is no civilian traffic in alleyways.
E	coastal road	A sandy, dusty, long road with sweeping bends. This road will have a parking lane and a single carriageway separated by a double yellow line.
F	mountain road	This road will comprise two wide lanes.
G	desert road	This road will be about the same size as the alleyway and will be a dusty, dirt track road, so traction might be a problem for the player.

Figure 75 Excerpt from the design proposal for a sequel game to Starsky and Hutch describing different roads that will be included in the game

Each one of the roads described above will have to be drawn and rendered in a 3D modelling package and have the required software code attached, for example the desert road may have code 'behind' it that makes the car slide all over the virtual track.

Frequently the written proposal document is accompanied by a mocked-up software disk that uses existing components and newly created drawings to give an idea of how the game might look and feel on-screen. For example, the specification of roads shown above is an improved version of the specification for roads that appeared in an earlier Starsky and Hutch game. On the mock-up disk the original drawings and coding were used to show how this aspect of the game might play.

5.5.3 Design document

Once a tender has been won the design proposal is further developed to provide a very detailed specification, which is a list of everything that needs to be created and considered for the game. This is known as the design document.

The drawing up of the design document can represent 40 per cent of the game designer's work on the project. The design document is developed by the lead artist, game designer and coder who meet with the producer to brainstorm ideas and work out the logic of the game and to ensure the plausibility of the game world that is to be created.

The group has to think through every step of the game to identify what needs to be developed and how tasks will be arranged on the schedule. This is done by creating simple flow charts and drawings and building up lists. Very occasionally storyboards will be used to convey ideas. The flow charts and drawings explore the main concept ideas for the game. In other words what the missions are that a game player has to undertake and what the player has to achieve at each level. Where possible, components from previous games are identified for reuse and consideration is given to how these might be adapted to the new project.

The design document develops the original design proposal into a specification. The document describes the characters, settings, and look and feel of the game. It also contains detailed descriptions of the structure of the story, rules for different levels of play of the game, controls, camera views and navigation (Figure 76).

The document also identifies all of the components that need to be designed for the game. The components include the following.

- Main characters, all of whom are generated in 3D graphics. The character details include information about what the characters can and cannot do.
- Interactive game objects are objects that do something when the player interacts with them, for example fire hydrants that burst open and spray water when crashed into or tokens that are collected along the way. These have to be drawn in 3D in all of their different modes, for example whole, at the point of impact and crashed.
- Other actors such as cars and pedestrians that may affect the playing of the game. These are all generated in 3D graphics.
- Static background images that do not do anything – they are the game equivalent of scenery. Although these are backdrops they will be seen from alternative camera angles and have to be located in the 3D world to make this possible.
- Maps of the terrain of the virtual world. For example, the Starsky and Hutch game takes place in an urban setting that covers over 24 square kilometres. This virtual city is divided into eight distinct areas such as Downtown, Dockside, and Chinatown, each with their own characteristics. The map is a vital part of the game development and informs the development of the other components listed above. For example, each district in the Starsky and Hutch map will have distinctive buildings, street furniture, people and conditions, all of which have to be designed and created.
- Time-related information such as the seasons and times of day in which the game is set that requires different lighting effects and extras such as snow, falling leaves and so on as part of the graphic landscape.
- Game features and effects, for example glowing headlights, street lights or smoke coming out of the player's car exhaust when accelerating.

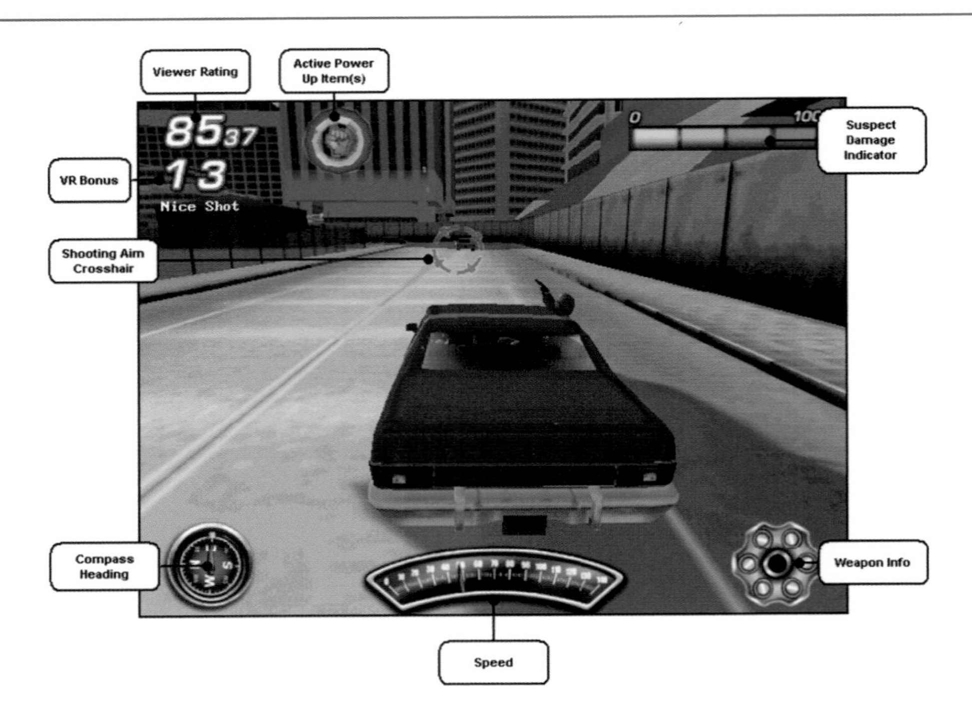

Status icons

Speed

The speedometer shows the vehicles' speed. There are no gears, so there is no need for a rev counter.

Viewer rating

This shows the current viewer rating for the player. The colour of the font changes dependent on the rating. Lower ratings are shown in red, while higher ratings are shown in blue.

Weapon information

The weapon info icon shows the currently available weapon and how many rounds remain. When the weapon is empty, the icon should change to indicate reloading is necessary.

Compass

Provides directional information showing which way the player is headed.

Compass beacon (part of the compass)

This icon appears as a flashing light on the compass to show the location of a suspect or location in comparison to the player.

Crosshair

The crosshair shows where Hutch is currently aiming (monoplay only). In both stereoplay and monoplay the crosshair will change or appear and indicate the target selected should not be shot at, for example when aiming at a hostage.

Pop-up icons

Target selector icon

The target selector icon shows the currently selected target(s) that is locked on and, (possibly) how accurate the shot is expected to be. There may be more than one target selector icon on screen, depending on which shooting method works best.

Danger icon

This icon appears whenever the player is in danger of being shot at by a suspect and will flash repeatedly until the player is out of danger.

Figure 76 Page from a proposal for a game visualising the player's view and functions seen on screen

In addition to the creation of the game itself the development team also has to design the tools to build it. Software tools known as editors are built to enable the designers to make changes to the components without having to start from scratch if a feature or character needs amendment. Developing the editor is the job of coders in conjunction with other members of the team.

5.5.4 Progressing the design

At the start of the design project a team of around 20 people is assembled from each of the three groups of artists, game designers and coders. The team have regular meetings to discuss the progress of the project. These take place in the Minds Eye meeting room, which presents an informal setting including comfortable sofas and a pool table. Progress of the project is marked by milestones that are set in conjunction with the external producer. The milestones are seen as essential in a complex long-term project. The setting of goals, which can be achieved in the short- to mid-term, enables team members to keep in step with one another.

Creating a game is a little like creating a film. Each game has scenes or episodes in which play takes place and groups of artists, game designers and coders are put together to work on specific elements. The office is arranged so that the people in each of these groups sit next to one another.

5.5.5 Creating the design

The development of the main characters of the game is the most complex piece of animation design. The starting point for the design of these characters is usually reference materials such as existing photos and drawings. The majority of games that Minds Eye works on are derived from television or films and so there is a lot of source material to inform the design. One of the first things that the managing director will do when working on the design proposal is to steep himself and his team in the subject in question, buying character toys, videos, books and so forth. A quick look around the office shows several character products and ephemera related to current and past projects.

The game designer will usually brief the lead artist on details of the character and the environment. Minds Eye sometimes commissions a 2D graphic artist on a freelance basis to draw possible characters as a starting point for the 3D design. At this early stage the lead artist also selects a colour palette and colour schemes that will be used to create the look and feel of the game.

Within the team of artists, there are a number of different roles each of which are crucial to the design process, these roles are:

- technical artist
- creative artist
- environment builders
- character builders
- animators

The technical artist has the responsibility of building the basic 3D frame of characters and objects. The technical artist works in conjunction with the creative artist to achieve the right look for each character. The character builders and animators take the work of the technical and creative artists and replicate and animate this for use throughout the game. The environment builders concentrate on creating the scenery of the game world.

5.5.6 Software tools

Once concept sketches have been generated and the overall look is agreed 3D drawing starts on the computer using 3D software called Maya, which is widely used in the games and animation industries. To develop a character, first a wire frame image is drawn and then skin and a texture are applied. Applying the skin and texture are done using a process called UV mapping. This process allows the textures that are applied to the 3D model to move with it giving a photo-realistic quality to the animation. To create realistic looking movements 'areas of influence' are identified. For example, if a character raises his arm it will influence the way his shoulder and chest move just as would happen in real life. In some games there may also be a need to synchronise characters' lip movements to speech. This is achieved by altering the mouth shape in reaction to certain parts of speech (phonemes) using a process known as morph targets.

The artists work almost exclusively straight onto their computer screens; very few hand drawn sketches are made. In addition to Maya they use Adobe PhotoShop for creating textures and skins. Each component or element of the game is built in the same way using a wireframe model first to create an internal framework and then adding the external skin and texture.

The work building the graphic components of the game takes the whole two years of the production process. As each component is completed it is added into the game-editing software. The editing tool enables the game to be continually rebuilt and played at the level of development so far. This facility enables the team to see the game as a whole entity at each stage of development showing the components that have been created in context and allowing them to be checked and signed off by the game designer. If problems are seen then adjustments can be made immediately.

The artists work on state of the art PCs and whoever has need for the greatest computing power at any one time will have the fastest PC. The lead artist scrutinises the artists' working methods to identify where time could be saved by better hardware or an automated process and ensure the artists have the tools needed for the job in hand. Artists may move from one role to another as jobs are completed and needs change.

The management of the multitude of components is highly complex and Minds Eye uses a piece of software called Alienbrain that assists this. Alienbrain tracks whether components have been completed or not; keeps files synchronised so that the up-to-date version is always to the fore but keeps all versions for reference; prevents team members from overwriting each other's files and enables comments to be entered against each component. This kind of management system is crucial when dealing with digital resources that could be wiped out at the click of a mouse.

5.5.7 Design for users

The majority of those involved in the design of games have been playing computer games since they were teenagers. The design teams frequently play other companies' games and see this not only as relaxation but also as a learning process. In particular they feel they have learned what mistakes to avoid by playing poor games.

The designers are designing for a predominantly adolescent male market and they are aware their products have limited appeal to women. Although the designers realise user testing away from the company could be a useful part of the development process, this is not built in. It is felt there is never enough time to do anything other than in-house testing.

In the development of the game design document the target audience is specified. Apart from those clearly targeted at a preschool market, most games are aimed at the 13- to 25-year-old male market, with an acknowledgement that older people and women may wish to play. Minds Eye's games do not contain graphic scenes of violence; this is done intentionally to extend the appeal of the games to as wide an audience as possible.

Beyond this, the design team has an awareness that in order for games to be successful players have to feel engaged and able to achieve the goals at each level of the game. Most games are designed with added extras, such as different modes of play to extend the game play and give added value to the product. For example, in the second Starsky and Hutch game there is a locker where the player can choose amusing extra vehicles, have a shoot out with skeletons or a race in a storm drain and find out more about the characters. There are also a number of cheat modes that change various components, for example all pedestrian characters are seen riding space hoppers.

5.5.8 Design outcome

At the end of the development process test disks are created that can be sent to the console manufacturers – Microsoft for Xbox, and Sony Europe and America for PlayStation. The console manufacturers employ testers to test the game play and may come back with requirements for amendment, though Minds Eye products usually pass this test routine first time. Once the agreement of the console manufacturers is obtained the gold master disk is handed over to the publisher.

The launch of products is the responsibility of the software publisher and it is crucial that the launch takes place at the right time; key points of the year are Thanksgiving and Christmas.

5.6 Evolving markets, technologies and design

The new market that is emerging is that for interactive television games. Creating games for this medium is constrained by hardware that is ten to fifteen years behind the technology used for console and PC games. In 2004 these games could not use the 3D graphics that are a necessary part of console games. Consequently the games are much smaller, more like the first generation of computer games. Like the first generation of computer games there are also far fewer people involved in the development process. Typically just an artist and a coder though a large game such as Tomb Raider also had a game designer involved throughout the project, as there was more than one level of play.

The company commissioning most interactive TV games in the UK is BSkyB though Minds Eye also produced a Big Brother game for the interactive Channel 4 station. The design team is given a design brief by the television company and then have one month to come up with a proof of concept that shows what is possible. The artist and coder work together, the coder works on the functionality of the game while the artist provides the components as they are needed. A producer makes sure the creative vision is maintained. The full development takes between two and six months and there is continual testing of the game throughout this time.

The design is all done using Adobe PhotoShop and because of the short timescales any work generated to test the concept is reused where possible.

Once developed, BSkyB uses an external testing house called Triple SL to test the end product and make sure there is consistency in functionality with other BSkyB products.

As computing technology has evolved, the development of games has become more and more complex. The first generation of games involved three people, the second generation ten to fifteen people and now the third generation can involve anywhere between 20 to 100 people. The next generation could involve twice as many again.

The technology has allowed more speed, so characters can talk, show emotion and interact with one another. Games are becoming more and more realistic looking and are becoming immersive in their feel. In other words the game world becomes a completely credible other world into which the game player steps. The latest game hardware such as the PlayStation EyeToy uses motion sensors and a camera to place an image of the player into the action on screen and this is likely to develop further.

Acknowledgements

Grateful acknowledgement is made to the following sources for permission to reproduce material within this book.

Illustrations

All figures in case study 1: © Dyson.
Figure 19: Thorpe Park.
Figure 22: Rui Vieira/PA Photos.
Figures 23 and 25: Alton Towers.
Figure 31: Courtesy of Bristol United Press.
Figure 33: Copyright www.offwell.info.
Figures 44 and 45: *Furniture and Cabinetmaking Magazine*/Chris Skorbon, GMC Publications.

Every effort has been made to contact copyright holders. If any have been inadvertently overlooked, the publishers will be pleased to make the necessary arrangements at the first opportunity.

Course Team

Academic staff

Ken Baynes, External Assessor
Catherine Cooke, Author
Nigel Cross, Author
Chris Earl, Author
Steve Garner, Author and Course Chair
Georgy Holden, Author
Robin Roy, Author

Consultants

Mike Ashby, Contributing Author, Block 5
Mark Evans, Contributing Author, Workbook 1
Tony Hodgson, Contributing Author, Block 5

Associate lecturers

Jenny Burke
Nick Jeffrey

Course managers

Andy Harding, Course Manager
Amber Thomas, Course Manager

Production staff

Tammy Alexander, Graphic Designer
Margaret Barnes, Course Secretary
Deirdre Bethune, Course Secretary
Philippa Broadbent, Print Buyer
Jane Bromley, Interactive Media Designer
Michael Brown, Video Editor
Daphne Cross, Assistant Print Buyer
Tony Duggan, Learning Projects Manager
Bernie D'Souza, Course Secretary
Vicky Eves, Graphic Artist
Barbara Fraser, Picture Researcher
Phil Gauron, Video Producer
Richard Hearne, Photographer
Lynda Jones, Rights Assistant
Jane Moore, Editor
Jonathon Owen, Graphic Artist
Val Price, Rights Executive
Alex Reid, Narrator (video)
Ekkehard Thumm, Media Project Manager
Robert Wood, Editor